BoE 7163

Hit Session 3

BoE 7163
HIT SESSION 3

ISBN 3-937041-74-5
ISMN M-2016-5024-1
Liedauswahl: Gerhard Hildner
Covergestaltung: Lars Bischof

BOSWORTH EDITION

BERLIN - LONDON

INHALT/CONTENTS

A WHITER SHADE OF PALE

♩	75	8 Ballad

Intro **C Em Am C F Am Dm F G G7 Em G7 C F G F G7**

```
    C       Em                          Am    C  F               Am                      Dm   F
1.     We skipped the light fandango        and turned cartwheels 'cross the floor.
    G           G7                      Em     G7 C         Em                   Am  C
       I was feeling kind of seasick,           the crowd called out for more.
    F         Am                          Dm     F G                G7             Em  G7
       The room was humming harder          as the ceiling flew away.
    C               Em                 Am      C       F       Am                    Dm
       When we called out for another drink,      the waiter brought a tray.
    G7              C  Em        Am    C  F           Am                Dm  F
    And so it was----- that later,         as the miller told his tale,
    G               G7                     Em   G7                  C      F               C   G4 G
        that her face at first just ghostly        turned a whiter      shade of pale.
```

Intro **C Em Am C F Am Dm F G G7 Em G7 C F G F G7**

```
    C       Em                       Am     C  F                Am                 Dm   F
2.     She said: "There is no reason,        and the truth is plain to see!"
    G           G7                              Em           G7 C          Em                  Am C
       But I wandered through my playing cards             and would not let her be.
    F             Am                    Dm     F G                 G7                  Em   G7
       One of sixteen Vestal Virgins,          who were leaving for the coast.
    C               Em        Am                   C  F           Am                          Dm
       And although my eyes were open,               they might just have well been closed.
    G7              C  Em        Am    C  F           Am                Dm  F
    And so it was----- that later,         as the miller told his tale,
    G               G7                     Em   G7                  C      F               C   G4 G
        that her face at first just ghostly        turned a whiter      shade of pale.
```

Intro *fade out*

F Am Dm F
and turned cart - wheels 'cross the floor.
G G7 Em G7
I was feel - ing kind of sea - sick,
C Em 3 Am C
the crowd called out for more.
F Am Dm F G G7
The room was humm - ing har - der as the ceil - ing flew a -
Em G7 C Em Am C
way. When we called out for a - no - ther drink,
F Am Dm G7 3 C Em
the wai-ter brought a tray. And so it was that la -
Am C F Am Dm F
- ter, as the mil - ler told his tale,
G G7 Em G7
that her face at first just ghost - ly turned a
C F C Gsus4 G
whi - ter shade of pale.
2x D.C.(2.mal fade out)

ALRIGHT

♩	94	Pop Rock

```
        G
1.        Wipe those tears away from your eyes.
        Am7
            Just take my hand, you don't have to cry,
              C                        G
        it'll be alright, baby, I'll make it alright.

        Don't let the world get you down,
        Am7
            reach for the love that's all around.
              C                          G
        It'll be alright, baby, we'll make it alright.

        Dm                            Am
Zw.         I'll pick you up when you're      feeling down,
        C                           G
          I'll put your feet back on    solid ground.
        Dm                         Am
            I'll pick you up and I'll     make you strong,
        C
            I'll make you feel like you still belong.

                    G
Ref.    'Cause it's alright, yeah, it's alright,
                        Am7
        let me make it alright, make it alright.
                             C                  G
        Stay with me tonight, stay with me tonight.

        G
2.         Sometimes the words, well, they're just not enough,
        Am7
             afraid of feelings and in need of love,
                    C                       G
        to make it alright, baby, I'll make it alright.

        Where will you run to, where will you hide?
        Am7
             I know the pain comes from deep down inside,
                    C                            G
        but it'll be alright, baby, we'll make it alright, Baby!

                        G
Ref.    Let me make it alright, make it alright.
                        Am7
        Let me make it alright, make it alright.
                             C                  G
        Stay with me tonight, stay with me tonight.

              G                             Am7
Br.     It's alright, yeah, it's alright. It's alright, yeah, it's alright.
              C                   G
        It's alright, to stay with me tonight.
```

Zw. **Dm** I'll pick you up when you're **Am** feeling down,
C I'll put your feet back on **G** solid ground.
Dm I'll pick you up and I'll **Am** make you strong,
C I'll make you feel like you still belong.

Ref. 'Cause it's **G** alright, yeah, it's alright,
let me make it **Am7** alright, make it alright.
Stay with me **C** tonight, stay with me **G** tonight.

Br. It's alright, yeah, it's alright. ... *(fade out)*

Am7
reach for the love that's all a - round. It - 'll be
C G
al-right, ba - by, we'll make it al - right.
Dm Am
I'll pick you up when you're feel - ing down,
C G
I'll put your feet back on so - lid ground.
Dm Am
I'll pick you up and I'll make you strong,
C
I'll make you feel like you still be - long. 'Cause it's al -
G
- right, yeah, it's al - right, let me make it al -
Am7
- right, make it al - right. Stay with me to -
C G D.C.
- night, stay with me to - night.

ANGIE

♩	70	Rock-Ballad

1.
Am E7 G F C Em
Angie, Angie when will those clouds all disappear? --
Am E7 G F C
Angie, Angie where will it lead us from here? --
G Dm Am
With no loving in our souls and no money in our coats.
C F G
Oh, you can't say we're satisfied. --
Am E7 G F C Em
Angie, Angie, you can't say we never tried. --

2.
Am E7 G F C Em
Uh, Angie, you're beautiful, yeah, but ain't it time we said goodbye? --
Am E7 G F C
Angie, I still love you, remember all those nights we cried. --
G Dm Am
All the dreams we held so close, seem to all go up in smoke.
C F G
Oh, let me whisper in your ear.
Am E7 G F C Em
Angie, Angie where will it lead us from here? --

3. *Instrumental* Am E7 G F C Em Am E7 G F C

G Dm Am
Oh, Angie don't you weep, all your kisses still taste sweet.
C F G
I hate that sadness in your eyes,
Am E7 G F C Em
but Angie, Angie ain't it time we said goodbye? --

4. *Instrumental* Am E7 G F C

G Dm Am
With no loving in our souls and no money in our coats.
C F G
Oh, you can't say we're satisfied.
Dm Am
But Angie, I still love you baby.
Dm Am
Everywhere I look I see your eyes.
Dm Am
There ain't a woman that comes close to you.
C F G
Come on baby dry your eyes!
Am E7 G F C Em
Angie, Angie ain't it good to be alive? --
Am E7 G F C
Angie, Angie, they can't say we never tried. –

Words & Music by Keith Richards, Mick Jagger

Am E7 G F
1.An-gie, An - gie when will those clouds all dis-ap - pear?
C Em Am E7
An-gie, An - gie
G F C
where will it lead us from here? With no
G Dm Am
lov-ing in our souls and no mo-ney in our coats.
C F G Am
Oh, you can't say we're sa-tis-fied. An-gie,
E7 G F
1./2.
C Em
An - gie, you can't say we ne-ver tried.
3.
C Em Am E7 G F C
bye? With no

G Dm Am
lov-ing in our souls and no mo-ney in our coats.
C F G
Oh, you can't say we're sa - tis - fied. But
Dm Am Dm
An gie, I still love you ba - by. Eve - ry - where I look I see your
Am Dm Am
eyes. There ain't a wo-man that comes close to you.
C F G Am
Come on ba - by dry your eyes! An - gie,
E7 G F C Em Am
An - gie ain't it good to be a - live? An - gie,
E7 G F C
An - gie they can't say we ne - ver tried!
rit.

AS TEARS GO BY

♩ 116 | Ballad

1.
G A7 C D
It is the evening of the day. –
G A7 C D
I sit and watch the children play. --
C D G D Em D
Smiling faces I can see, but not for me.
C D
I sit and watch as tears go by.

2.
G A7 C D
My riches can't buy everything, --
G A7 C D
I want to hear the children sing. --
C D G D Em D
All I hear is the sound of rain falling on the ground.
C D
I sit and watch as tears go by.

3. *Instrumental*

4.
G A7 C D
It is the evening of the day. –
G A7 C D
I sit and watch the children play. –
C D G D Em D
Doing things I used to do they think are new.
C D
I sit and watch as tears go by.

5.
G
Mmh, mmh, ... *(summen, fade out)*

Words & Music by Mick Jagger, Keith Richards

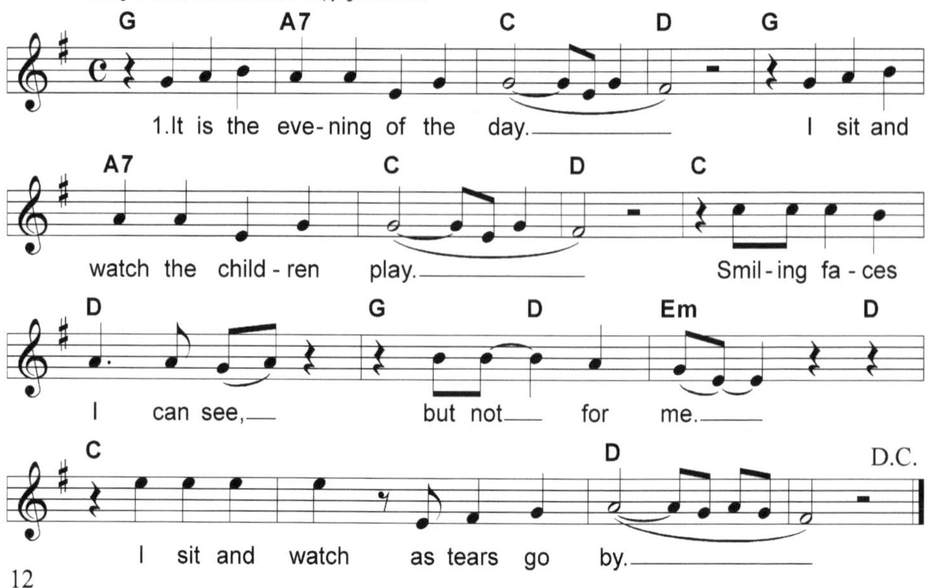

ATLANTIS

♩ 80 | Rock-Ballad

1.
C
The continent of Atlantis was an island,
D
which lay before the great flood
FMaj7
in the area we now call the Atlantic Ocean.
C G C
So great an area of land, that from her western shores
D
those beautiful sailors journeyed to the South and the North Americas with ease,
FMaj7 C G
In their ships with painted sails.
C D FMaj7
To the east Africa was a neighbour, across a short strait of sea miles.
C G
The great Egyptian age is but a remnant of the Atlantian culture.
C
The antediluvian kings colonised the world,
D
all the Gods who play in the mythological dramas,
FMaj7 C G
in all legends from all lands were from fair Atlantis.
C D
Knowing her fate, Atlantis sent out ships to all corners of the earth.
FMaj7
On board were the Twelve: The poet, the physician, the farmer, the scientist,
C G
the magician and the other so called Gods of our legends.
C D
Though Gods they were, and as the elders of our time choose to remain blind,
FMaj7 C G
let us rejoice and let us sing and dance and ring in the new. Hail Atlantis!

Ref.
C D F C G
//: Way down below the ocean where I wanna be she may be. :// *(fade out)*

BABY, I'D LOVE YOU TO WANT ME

♩	79	16 Ballad

```
     G
1.      When I saw you standin' there
                           Am
     I 'bout fell off my chair,
                                              C
     and when you moved your mouth to speak
     D                      G
        I felt the blood go to my feet.

                                  G
2.   Now it took time for me to know
                                 Am
     what you tried so not to show.
                                  C
     Somethin' in my soul just cries,
     D                           G
        I see the want in your blue eyes.

       G                   Am
Ref. Baby, I'd love you to want me
                    C                          G
     the way that I want you, the way that it should be.
                              Am
     Baby, you'd love me to want you
                     C             D         G
     the way that  I want to, if you'd only let it be.

                              G
3.   You told yourself years ago
                                     Am
     you'd never let your feelings show.
                              C
     The obligation that you made
     D                        G
        for the title that they gave.


Ref. Baby, I'd love you to want me ...

2.   Now it took time for me to know ...

Ref. Baby, I'd love you to want me ...    (fade out)
```

Words & Music by Kent Lavoie

G
G
1.When I saw you stand-in' there I 'bout fell off my
Am
C
chair, and when you moved your mouth to speak
D
G
I felt the blood go to my feet.
G
2.Now it took time for me to know
Am
what you tried so not to show. Some-thin' in my soul just
C
D
G
cries, I see the want in your blue eyes.
G
Am
Ba - by, I'd love you to want me the way that I want
C
G
you, the way that it should be. Ba - by, you'd love me to want
Am
C
you the way that I want to, if you'd
D
G
D.S.and fade out (im Refrain)
on - ly let it be. 3.You told your - self years a -

BED OF ROSES

♩. | 55 | Slow Rock

```
       B♭                                        F
1.     Sitting here wasted and wounded at this old piano.
            B♭                                       F
       Trying hard to capture the moment, this morning I don't know.
                Am                     B♭
       'Cause a bottle of vodka is still lodged in my head
                 F                                                     B♭
       and some blond gave me nightmares, I think that she's still in my bed.
                                          C7                     F
       As I dream about movies they won't make of me when I'm dead.

            B♭                                         F
2.     With an iron-clad fist I wake up and french-kiss the morning.
                 B♭                                                    F
       While some marching band keeps it's own beat in my head while we're talking
            Am                      B♭
       about all of the things that I long to believe,
            F                                              B♭
       about love, the truth, what you mean to me and the truth is:
                C7           F     C
       "Baby you're all that I need!"

              Dm      C         B♭     F
Ref.   I wanna lay you down in a bed of roses.
            Dm      C        B♭     F
       For tonight I sleep on a bed of nails.
                 B♭         F          B♭     F
       Oh, I wanna be just as close as the Holy Ghost is
           Dm C   B♭             F
       and lay you down on a bed of roses.

              B♭                               F
3.     Well I'm so far away, each step that I take on my way home .
              B♭                                                F
       A king's ransom in dimes I'd give each night to see through this payphone.
            Am                 B♭
       Still I run out of time or it's hard to get through
            F
       till the bird on the wire flies me back to you.
          B♭                                  C7              F    C
       I'll just close my eyes and whisper: "Baby blind love is true!"

Ref.   I wanna lay you down ...

                B♭                   C
Zw.    Well, this hotel bar hangover whiskey's gone dry.
              F
       The barkeeper's wig's crooked, and she's giving me the eye.
              B♭                                    C7       F    C
       Well, I might have said yes, but I laughed so hard I think I died.

Solo   Dm  C  B♭ F   Dm  C B♭ F   Dm  C B♭ F   Dm C B♭   F
```

4. **B♭** **F**
Now as you close your eyes know I'll be thinking about you.
B♭ **F**
While my mistress she calls me to stand in her spotlight again.
B♭ **F**
Tonight I won't be alone, but you know that don't mean I'm not lonely.
Dm **C** **B♭** **F** **C**
I've got nothing to prove, for it's you that I'd die to defend.

Ref. I wanna lay you down ... *(2x)*

F
dead.
Bb
2.With an i - ron - clad fist I wake up and french - kiss the
F
mor - ning.
Bb
While some march - ing band keeps it's own beat in my head while we're
F
talk-ing
Am
a - bout all of the things that I
Bb
long to be-lieve, a - bout
F
love, the truth, what you mean to me and the
Bb
truth is:
C7
"Ba - by you're all that I
F
need!"
C
I wan - na
Dm
lay
C
you down
Bb
in a bed of
F
ro - ses.
For to -
Dm
night
C
I sleep
Bb
on a bed of
F
nails.
Oh, I wan - na
Bb
be
F
just as close as
Bb
the Ho - ly
F
Ghost is
and
Dm
lay
C
you
Bb
down
on a bed of
F
ro - ses.
Fine
D.S.al
3.Well I'm
18

F C B♭ C
ro- ses. Well, this ho - tel bar hang - o - ver whis - key's gone dry. The bar -
F
kee - per's wig's crooked, and she's giv - ing me the eye. Well, I
B♭ C7
might have said yes, but I laughed so hard I think I
F C Dm C B♭ F
died.
Dm C B♭ F Dm C B♭ F
Dm C B♭ F
D.S.al Fine
4.Now as

BEHIND BLUE EYES

♩	60	Rock-Ballad

Em G D
1. No one knows what it's like to be the bad man,
C A
to be the sad man, behind blue eyes.
Em G D
And no one knows what it's like to be hated,
C A
to be fated to telling only lies.

C D G C D E
Ref. But my dreams -- they aren't as empty as my conscience seems to be.
Bm C D A2
I have hours, only lonely, my love is vengeance, that's never free.

Em G D
2. No one knows what it's like to feel these feelings,
C A
like I do and I blame you.
Em G D
No one bites back as hard on their anger
C A
none of my pain and woe can show through. *Ref. But my dreams ...*

Em G D
Zw. (gespr.:) *Discover!* **//:** *L-I-M-P, say it: Discover!*
CMaj7 A2
L-I-M-P, say it: Discover! **://**

Em G D
3. No one knows what it's like to be mistreated,
C A
to be defeated behind blue eyes.
Em G D
And no one knows how to say that they're sorry
C A
and don't worry I'm not telling lies. *Ref. But my dreams ...*

Em G D
4. No one knows what it's like to be the bad man,
C A
to be the sad man, behind blue eyes.

Em G D
no one knows what it's like to be hat - ed, to be
C A
fat - ed to tell - ing on - ly lies. But my
C D G
dreams they aren't as emp - ty as my
C D E Bm
con - science seems to be. I have hours, on - ly lone -
C D
- ly, my love is ven - geance, that's ne - ver
1. Asus2 2. Asus2
free. free. Dis-cov-er!
Em G D CMaj7
L - I - M - P, say it: Dis-cov-er! L - I - M -
Asus2 D.C.al Coda (ohne Wdhl.) Asus2
P, say it: Dis-cov-er! free.
Em G D
4.No one knows what it's like to be the bad man, to be the
C A
sad man, be - hind blue eyes.

BEDS ARE BURNING

♩	136	Techno-Beat

1. D Out where the river broke, the bloodwood and the desert oak,
holden wrecks and boiling diesels, steam in forty-five degrees.

Zw. The time has come to say fair's fair, to pay the rent, to pay our share. (D – C/D – G/D – D)
The time has come a fact's a fact, it belongs to them let's give it back. (C/D – G/D – E – D F G)

Ref. How can we dance when our earth is turning? (Dm – B♭ – F)
How do we sleep while our beds are burning? (Dm – B♭ – C – C♯0)
How can we dance when our earth is turning? (Dm – B♭ – F)
How do we sleep while our beds are burning? (Dm – B♭ – C – C♯0)

Zw. The time has come to say fair's fair, to pay the rent, now to pay a share. (Dm – B♭ – F – C – D F G)

2. D Four wheels scare the cockatoos from Kintyre East to Yuendemu.
The western desert lives and breathes in forty-five degrees.

Zw. The time has come ...

Ref. How can we dance when our earth is turning? ...

Zw. The time has come to say fair's fair, to pay the rent, to pay our share. (Dm – B♭ – F – C)
The time has come a fact's a fact, it belongs to them let's give it back. (Dm – B♭ – F – C)

Ref. How can we dance when our earth is turning? ...

Outro **Dm B♭ F C Dm B♭ F C D F G**

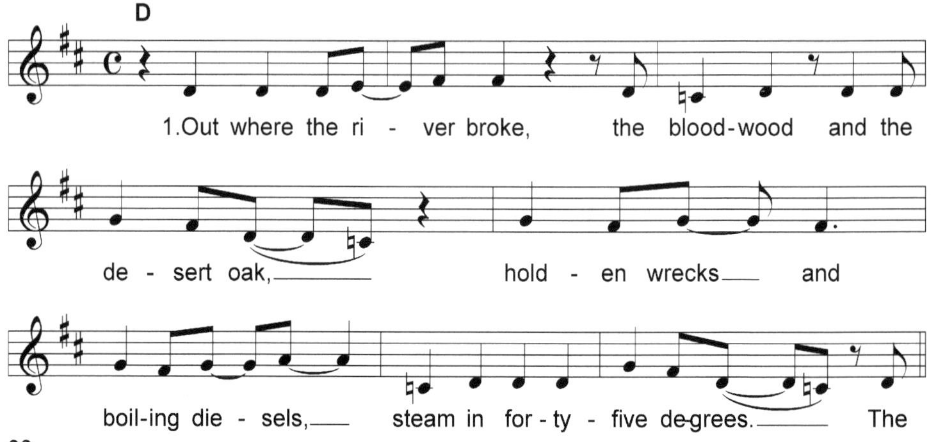

D C/D
time has come to say fair's fair, to
G/D D
pay the rent, to pay our share.
The time has come a
C/D G/D
fact's a fact, it be - longs to them let's
E D F G
give it back.
Dm B♭ F
How can we dance when our earth is turn - ing?
Dm B♭ C
How do we sleep while our beds are burn-ing?
C♯° Dm B♭
How can we dance when our earth is turn-ing?
F Dm
How do we sleep while our
B♭ C C♯° Dm
beds are burn-ing? The time has come to

Words & Music by Peter Garrett, Robert Hirst & James Moginie

BLACK VELVET

♩	91	Rock Shuffle

```
      Em
1.       Mississippi in the middle of a dry spell,

      Jimmy Rodgers on the Victrola up high.

      Mama's dancin' with baby on her shoulder,

      the sun is settin' like molasses in the sky.
      B4                B            A4   A
        The boy could sing, knew how to move,    everything,
      G4          G          D4
        always wanting more,      he'd leave you longing for

      Am7                      D4         D
Ref.       Black velvet and that little boy smile.
      Am7                          F            C
           Black velvet with that slow southern style.
      Am7                          D4                D
           A new religion that'll bring ya to your knees.
      C7         B7            Em
        Black velvet if you please.

      Em
2.       Up in Memphis the music's like a heat wave.

      White lightnin', bound to drive you wild.

      Mama's baby is in the heart of every school girl,

      "Love me tender" leaves 'em cryin' in the aisle.
      B4                B          A4       A
        The way he moved it was a sin, so sweet and true.
      G4          G          D4
        Always wanting more.      He'd leave you longing for

Ref.  Black velvet ...

      Am                         B7                      Em
Br.     Every word of every song that he sang was for you.
      Am                       F                C
         In a flash he was gone, it happened so soon,
      B7                 Em
         what could you do?

Solo  (Em)

Ref.  Black velvet ...   (2x)

         Em
      //:        If you please! ://(Wdhl. ad lib., fade out)
```

Em
1.Mis-sis-sip-pi in the mid-dle of a dry spell,
Jim-my Rod-gers on the Vic-tro-la up high.
Ma-ma's danc-in' with ba-by on her shoul-der,
the sun is set-tin' like mo-las-ses in the sky.
Bsus4 B Asus4 A
The boy could sing, knew how to move, eve-ry-thing,
Gsus4 G Dsus4
al-ways want-ing more, he'd leave you long-ing for
Am7 Dsus4 D
Black vel-vet and that lit-tle boy smile.
Am7 F C
Black vel-vet with that slow south-ern style.

Am7
Dsus4
3
D
A new re - li - gion that-'ll bring ya to your knees.
C7
B7
1.
Em
2
Black vel - vet if you please.
2.
Em
Am
Eve - ry word of eve - ry song
please.
B7
Em
that he sang was for you.
Am
F
C
In a flash he was gone, it hap-pened so soon,
B7
Em
Em
6
what could you do?
Em
Em
please.
If you please!
Wdhl. ad lib., dann fade out

BREAKFAST IN AMERICA

♩	73	Pop Ballad

Am G F G
1. Take a look at my girlfriend, she's the only one I got.
Am G F
Not much of a girlfriend, I never seem to get a lot.
E7 Am
Take a jumbo 'cross the water, like to see America,
E7 Dm7 G
See the girls in California. I'm hoping it's going to come true,
Dm7 G
but there's not a lot I can do.

Am G F G
2. Could we have kippers for breakfast, mummy dear, mummy dear?
Am G F
They got to have 'em in Texas, 'cause every one's a millionaire.
E7 Am
I'm a winner, I'm a sinner, do you want my autograph?
E7 Dm7 G
I'm a loser, what a joker. I'm playing my jokes upon you
Dm7 G
while there's nothing better to do.

E7 Am
Ref. Ba-ba-da-da, ba-ba-da, ba-ba-da-di-da-di-da.
E7 Am
Ba-ba-da-da, ba-ba-da, ba-ba-da-di-da-di-da.
G F Em Dm7 G
Na na na, na na na na na na na. *1.Don't you look at my girlfriend, ...*

E7 Am
Ref. Ba-ba-da-da, ba-ba-da, ba-ba-da-di-da-di-da.
E7 Am
Ba-ba-da-da, ba-ba-da, ba-ba-da-di-da-di-da.
E7 Am
Hey, oh! Hey, oh! Hey, oh! Hey, oh!
E7 Am
Hey, oh! Hey, oh! Hey, oh! Hey, oh!
G F Em Dm7 G
Na na na, na na na na na na na.

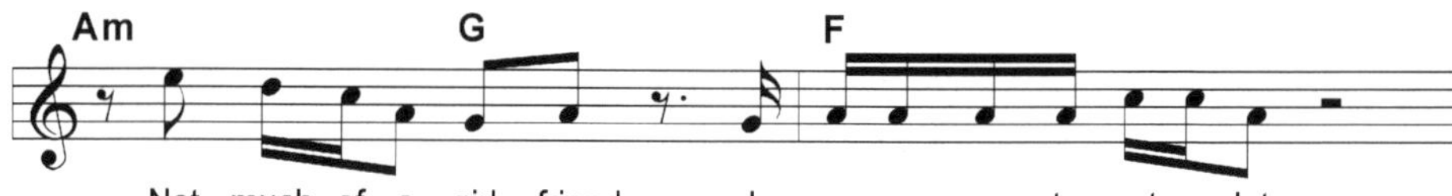

E7 Am
Take a jum-bo 'cross the wa-ter, like to see A-me-ri-ca,
E7 Dm7 G
See the girls in Ca-li-for-nia. I'm hop-ing it's going to come true, but there's
Dm7 G E7
not a lot I can do. Ba-ba-da-da, ba-ba-da, ba-ba-
Am E7
da-di da di-da. Ba-ba-da-da, ba-ba-da, ba-ba-
Am G F Em Dm7 G
da-di-da-di-da. Na na na, na na na na na na na.
D.C.al
Am
da-di-da-di-da. Hey,
E7 Am
oh! Hey, oh! Hey, oh! Hey, oh! Hey,
E7 Am G
oh! Hey, oh! Hey, oh! Hey, oh! Na na
F Em Dm7 G
na, na na na na na na na.

BRIGHT EYES

♩	57	16 Ballad

Intro **G Em Bm7 C7 G**

1.
G C G Em C G
Is it a kind of dream -- floating out on the tide, --
D D7 G C Am D
following the river of death downstream, or is it a dream?
G C G Em C G
There's a fog along the horizon, a strange glow in the sky, --
D D7 G C B
and nobody seems to know where it goes and what does it mean,
E^0 G D7 G
oh, oh, is it a dream?

Ref.
Bm C D
Bright eyes, burning like fire,
Bm C Am
bright eyes, how can you close and fail?
B7 Em D G
How can the light that burned so brightly,
C Am D7 G
suddenly burn so pale? Bright eyes!

Zw. **(G) Em C**

2.
G C G Em C G
Is it a kind of a shadow reaching into the night, --
D D7 G C Am D
wondering over the hills unseen, or is it a dream?
G C G Em C G
There's a high wind in the trees, -- a cold sound in the air, --
D D7 G C B
and nobody ever knows when you go and where do you start,
E^0 G D7 G
oh, oh, into the dark.

Ref. Bright eyes, burning like fire, ... ***(2x)***

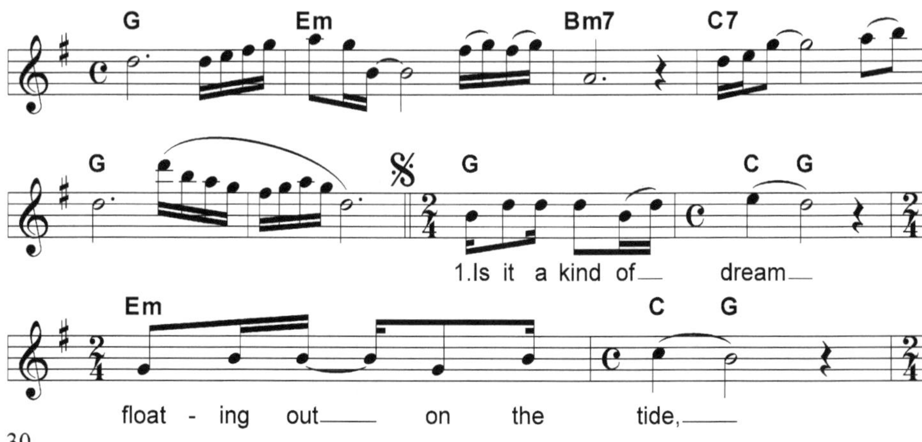

D D7 G C Am
fol-low-ing the riv-er of death down-stream, or is it a
D G C G
dream? There's a fog a-long the ho-ri - zon, a
Em C G
strange glow in the sky, and
D D7 G C
no-bo-dy seems to know where it goes and what does it
B E○ G D7 G
mean, oh, oh, is it a dream? Bright eyes,
Bm C D
burn - ing like fi - re, bright eyes,
Bm C Am
how can you close and fail?
B7 Em D G
How can the light that burned so bright - ly,
C Am D7 G
sud - den - ly burn so pale? Bright eyes!
Em C
D.S. 𝄋

BRING ME SOME WATER

♩ 126 Pop Rock

```
    Am
1.        Tonight I feel so weak but all in love is fair.

    I turn the other cheek and I feel the slap and a sting of the foul night air.
           Dm                                   Am
    And I know you're only human, and I haven't got talking room.
          Dm                                  E
    But tonight while I'm making excuses    some other woman is making love to yo

    A             G               D     A             G       D
Ref.1  Somebody bring me some water, can't you see I'm burning alive?
      A                  G    D                    A          G        D
    Can't you see my baby's got another lover?   I don't know how I'm gonna surviv
    A             G               D     A             G          D
       Somebody bring me some water, can't you see it's out of control.
      A            G               D
    Baby's got my heart, and my baby's got my mind,
         E                                    Am
    but tonight a sweet devil, sweet devil's got my soul.

    (Am)
2.       When will this aching pass, when will this night be through?

    I wanna hear the breaking glass, I wanna feel the steel of the red hot truth.
        Dm
    And I'll do anything to get it out of my mind,
          Am
    I need some insanity that temporary kind.
     Dm
    Tell me, how will I ever be the same,
              E
    when I know that woman is whispering your name?

    A             G               D     A             G       D
Ref.2  Somebody bring me some water, can't you see I'm burning alive?
      A                  G    D
    Can't you see my baby's got another lover?
       E                            D
    And I don't know how I'm gonna survive.
    A             G               D     A             G          D
       Somebody bring me some water, can't you see it's out of control.
      A            G               D
    Baby's got my heart, and my baby's got my mind,
         E                                    F#m
    but tonight a sweet devil, sweet devil's got my soul.

Zw.  (F#m)  G  A   F#m  G  A   F#m  G  A   G/B  D  E

    A             G               D                A  G  D  A  G  D
Ref.2  Somebody bring me some water, ...   ... got my soul. ------

      A            G               D
    Baby's got my heart, and my baby's got my mind,
         E                                    A7
    but tonight a sweet devil, sweet devil's got my soul.
```

Am
1.To-night I feel so weak but all in love is
fair. I turn the o-ther cheek and I feel the
Dm
slap and a sting of the foul night air. And I know you're on-ly
Am
3 3
hu-man, and I ha-ven't got talk-ing room. But to-
Dm
3 3
E
night while I'm mak-ing ex-cus-es some o-ther wo-man is
A G
mak-ing love to you. Some-bo-dy bring me some wa-
D A G D
-ter, can't you see I'm burn-ing a-live?
A G D
Can't you see my ba-by's got a-no-ther lo-ver?
A G D
I don't know how I'm gon-na sur-vive.

A G D
Some - bo - dy bring me some wa - ter, can't
A G D
you see it's out of con - trol.
A G D
Ba - by's got my heart, and my ba - by's got my mind, but to -
E Am
night a sweet de - vil, sweet de - vil's got my soul.
D.C.al Φ1
Φ1
A G D
Some - bo - dy bring me some wa - ter, can't
A G D
you see I'm burn - ing a - live?
A G D
Can't you see my ba - by's got a - no - ther lo - ver? And
E D
I don't know how I'm gon - na sur - vive.

A G D
Some - bo - dy bring me some wa - ter, can't
A G D
you see it's out of con - trol.
A G D
Ba - by's got my heart, and my ba - by's got my mind, but to -
E 2 F♯m G
night a sweet de - vil, sweet de - vil's got my soul.
A F♯m G A F♯m G A
G/B D E
D.S.al 2
2 A G
soul.
D A G D A G
Ba - by's got my heart, and my
D E
ba - by's got my mind, but to - night a sweet de - vil,
A7
sweet de - vil's got my soul.
rit.

BROTHERS IN ARMS

♩	79	16 Ballad

```
        Am          C                F   G                    C  C4 C
1.          These mist covered mountains, are a home now for me.
              Em          Am Em                  F
        But my home is the lowlands, and always will be.
        G4        G          Am  Em                      F     Dm  G4
           Some day you'll return to your valleys and your farms.
                  G        Am        F         G4     G
        And you'll no longer burn to be brothers in arms.

Zw.     Am  F  Dm  F  Am  F  Dm  Am

        Am                   C              F  G                C   C4 C
2.          Through these fields of destruction, Baptism of fire.
            Em                Am  Em                      F
        I've witnessed your suffering, as the battles raged higher.
        G4         G                Am       Em                    F    Dm  G4
            And though they did hurt me so bad, in the fear and alarm.
            G          Am          F          G4      G
        You did not desert me, my brothers in arms.

Zw.     Am  F  Dm  F  Am  F  Dm  Am

        Am               G               Am    G      C              F
Br.        There's so many different worlds,    so many different suns.
        G4        G               Am   G          C              F
           And we have just one world,      but we live in different ones.

Zw.     //: Am  F  Dm  F  Am  F  Dm :// Am

        Am              C            F  G                     C   C4 C
3.         Now the sun's gone to hell and the moon's riding high.
             Em            Am  Em                    F
        Let me bid your farewell,        every man has to die.
        G4              G            Am Em                      F    Dm  G4
           But it's written in the starlight and every line in your palm:
             G             Am          F          G4     G
        We're fools to make war on our brothers in arms.

Outro   //: Am  F  Dm  F  Am  F  Dm :// (fade out)
```

Am Em F
- lands, and al - ways will be.
Gsus4 G Am Em
Some day you'll re - turn to your val - leys and your
F Dm Gsus4 G
farms. And you'll no lon - ger
Am F Gsus4 G Am F Dm F
burn to be bro - thers in arms.
Am F Dm Am Am G
There's so ma - ny diffe - rent
Am G C F
worlds, so ma-ny diffe-rent suns.
Gsus4 G Am G C
And we have just one world, but we live in diffe - rent
F Am F Dm F Am F Dm
ones.
Am Am F Dm F Am F Dm
Wdhl. ad lib., dann fade out
D.C.al Coda

COTTONFIELDS

♩ 148 | Country-Rock

Vers
```
    G
When I was a little bitty baby,
       G7            C                G
my mama would rock me in the cradle,
                                   D7
in them old cotton fields back home.
          G
It was down in Louisiana,
 G7            C              G
just about a mile from Texarkana,
                D7               G    C G
in them old cotton fields back home.
```

Ref.
```
         G7      C
Oh, when them cotton balls get rotten,
           G
you can't pick very much cotton,
                                   D7
in them old cotton fields back home.
          G
It was down in Louisiana,
 G7            C             G
just about a mile from Texarkana,
                D7               G    C G
in them old cotton fields back home.
```

Musik und Text: trad.

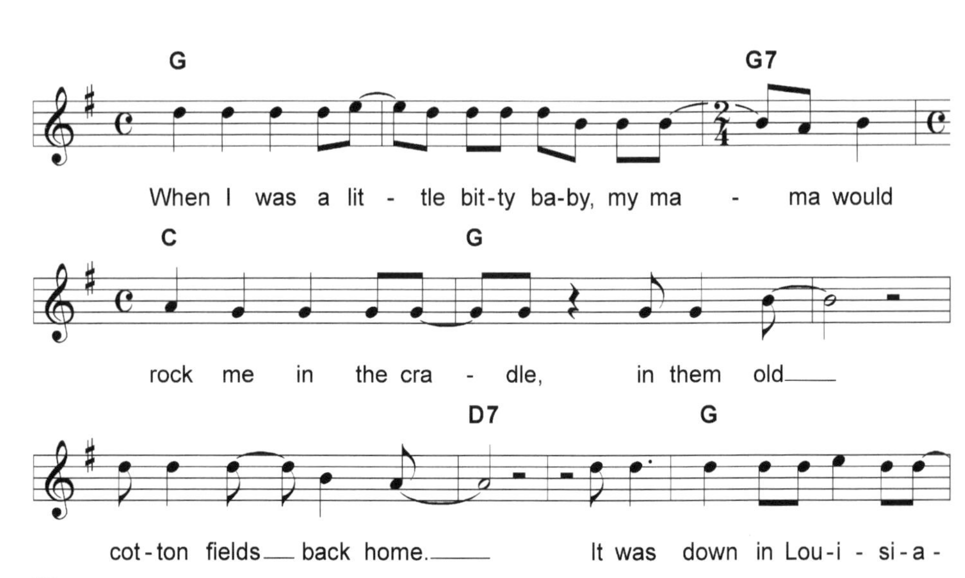

G7 C G
- na, just a - bout a mile from Tex-ar - ka - na, in them old
D7 G C G G7
cot-ton fields back home. Oh, when them
C G
cot-ton balls get rot-ten, you can't pick ve - ry much
D7
cot - ton, in them old cot-ton fields back home.
G G7
It was down in Lou - i - si - a - na, just a - bout a
C G
mile from Tex - ar - ka - na, in them old
D7 G C G
D.C.
cot - ton fields back home.

CRAZY

♩.	54	12/8 Blues Slow Rock

```
                              G                                     Em
Intro   Come 'ere baby!          You know you drive me up the wall.
                                                        C
        The way you make good on all the nasty tricks you pull
                                      Cm
        seems like we're makin' up more than we're makin' love.
        G                                  Em
           And it always seems you got somethin' on your mind other than me.
        C                                Cm
          Girl, you got to change your crazy ways. You hear me?

        G                  C
1.         Say you're leavin' on a seven thirty train
                                  Em          C
        and that you're headin' out to Hollywood.
        G                           C
           Girl you been givin' me the line so many times
                            Em              C
        it kinda gets like feelin' bad looks good.
        D               Em              F         C
           That kinda lovin' turns a man to a slave.
        D               Em                F                   C    D
           That kinda lovin' sends a man right to his grave.

             G       Em    C          Cm
Ref.1   I go crazy, crazy, baby, I go crazy.
        G                Em               C
           You turn it on, then you're gone.
                      D          G       Em     C              Cm
        Yeah, you drive me crazy, crazy, crazy for you baby.
        Am                D           B7                  Em D   C  Cm
             What can I do, honey?        I feel like the color blue.----

        G                            C
2.        You're packin up your stuff and talkin like it's tough
             Em                                   C
        and tryin to tell me that it's time to go.
        G                            C                                Em
           But I know you ain't wearin' nothin' underneath that overcoat
                          C
        and it's all a show.
        D                Em                          F                C
          That kinda lovin' makes me wanna pull down the shade, yeah.
        D                 Em                         F                              C
          That kinda lovin', yeah, now I'm never, never, never, never gonna be the same.
```

Ref.1   I go crazy, ...

```
        G                   Em             C            D
Zw.        I'm losin' my mind, girl, 'cause I'm goin' crazy.
```

Zw. //: G Em C Cm G Em C D7 ://

Br.
Em D C Cm Em D C
I need your love, honey. Yeah, I need your love.

Ref.2
G Em C Cm
//: Crazy, crazy, crazy for you baby.
G Em C D
I'm losin' my mind, girl, 'cause I'm goin' crazy.
G Em C Cm
Crazy, crazy, crazy for you baby.
G Em C D
You turn it on, then you're gone. Yeah you drive me ... :// *(fade out)*

G Em C Cm G Em C Cm

Intro-Sprechteil siehe Textseite!

G C
1.Say you're leav-in' on a se-ven thir-ty train and that you're head-in'
Em C
out to Hol - ly - wood.
G C
Girl you been giv-in' me the line so ma-ny times it kind-a gets like
Em C D Em
feel-in' bad looks good. That kind-a lov-in' turns a
F C D Em
man to a slave. That kind-a lov-in' sends a

F C D G Em
man right to his grave. I go cra - zy, cra - zy,
C Cm G Em
ba - by, I go cra - zy. You turn it on, then you're
C D G Em
gone. Yeah, you drive me cra - zy, cra - zy,
C Cm Am D
cra - zy for you ba - by. What can I do, ho - ney?
B7 Em D C Cm
I feel like the co - lor blue.
G Em C D
I'm los - in' my mind, girl, 'cause I'm go - in' cra - zy.
G Em C Cm G Em C D7
Em D C Cm
I need your love, ho - ney.
Em D C D.S.
Yeah, I need your love.

DANCING IN THE STREET

♩ 131 Rhythm & Blues

C7
1. Calling out around the world, are you ready for a brand new beat?
Summer's here and the time is right for dancing in the street.
They're dancing in Chicago, down in New Orleans, in New York City.

F
Br. All we need is music, sweet music.
There'll be music everywhere.
C7
They'll be swinging and swaying, records playing,
dancing in the street. Oh!

E7 Am
Ref. It doesn't matter what you wear, just as long as you are there.
D7 G7
So come on, every guy, grab a girl, everywhere, around the world.
C7
They'll be dancing, dancing in the street.

C7
2. Well, it's an invitation across the nation, a chance for folks to meet.
They'll be laughing and singing and music swinging, dancing in the street.
Philadelphia PA., Baltimore and D.C. now. Don't forget the Motor City,
on the streets of Brazil, back in the U.S.S.R., no matter where you are.

Br. All we need is music, ...

Ref. It doesn't matter ...

C7
Outro //: Way down in L.A., everyday, dancing in the street,
across in China too, me and you, dancing in the street.
Don't you know they'll be dancing, dancing in the street? :// *(fade out)*

C7
1.Call - ing out a - round the world, are you
rea - dy for a brand new beat?
Sum - mer's here and the
time is right for dan - cing in the street.
They're dan - cing in Chi - ca - go,
down in
New Or - leans,
in New York Ci - ty.
F
All we need is mu - sic, sweet mu - sic.
There'll be
mu - sic eve - ry - where.
They'll be swing - ing and sway - ing,
C7
3
re - cords play - ing, dan - cing in the street.
Oh!
E7
It does - n't mat - ter what you wear, just as long

Am
D7
as you are there. So come on, eve - ry guy,
G7
grab a girl, eve - ry - where, a -
C7
round the world. They'll be dan - cing, dan-cing in the street.
1.
2.
2.Well, it's an Way down in L. A.,
C7
e - ve - ry - day, dan - cing in the street,
a-cross in Chi-na too, me and you, dan-cing in the street.
Don't you know they'll be dan - cing,
fade out
dan-cing in the street? Way down in L. A.,

DAS SPIEL

♩	143	(Folk) Waltz

1.
C Am
Dass du nicht mehr bist, was du einmal warst,
F G
seit du dich für mich ausgezogen hast,
C Am
dass du alles schmeißt wegen einer Nacht
F G
und alles verlierst, war so nicht gedacht.
C F
Du willst mich für dich und du willst mich ganz,
Am G
doch auf dem Niveau macht's mir keinen Spaß.
C Am F
Das füllt mich nich' aus, ich fühl' mich zuhaus nur zwischen den Stühl'n.

Ref.
G C Am F G C Am F
Ich will doch nur spiel'n. Hmm! ---- Hmm! ---- Ich tu' doch nichts. ----
G C Am F G C Am (F G)
Ich will doch nur spiel'n. Hmm! ---- Hmm! ---- Ich tu' doch nichts. -------

2.
C Am
Dass du wegen mir irgendwen verlässt,
F G
dass du manchmal weinst, weil es dich verletzt,
C Am
dass es immer mal jemand andern gibt,
F G
der sich hier und da in mein Leben schiebt.
C F
Dass du dich verliebst, weil du's mit mir tust,
Am G
dass es dich so trifft, hab ich nicht gewusst.
C Am F
Es war nie geplant, dass du dich jetzt fühlst wie einer von viel'n. ***Ref. ...***

Zw. **C Am F G C Am F G C Am F G C Am F G**

3.
C Am
Dass du nich' mehr schläfst, weil es dich erregt,
F G
wenn ich mich beweg' wie ich mich beweg',
C Am
dass du fast verbrennst unter meiner Hand,
F G
wenn ich dich berühr' hab ich nich' geahnt.
C F
Ich steh' nur so rum, tu' so dies und das,
Am G
fahr mir durch das Haar und schon willst du was.
C Am F
Lass mal lieber sein, hab zuviel Respekt vor dein'n Gefühl'n. ***Ref. ...***

F G C Am F G C Am F G C Am
Ich tu' doch nichts. Ich will doch nur spiel'n. ---
F G C Am F G C
Ich tu' doch nichts. ---- Ich tu' doch nichts.

C Am
1.Dass du nicht mehr bist, was du ein - mal warst, seit du dich für
F G C
mich aus-ge-zo-gen hast, dass du al - les schmeißt we-gen ei - ner
Am F G
Nacht und al - les ver - lierst, war so nicht ge - dacht. Du willst mich für
C F Am
dich und du willst mich ganz, doch auf dem Ni - veau macht's mir kei-nen
G C Am
Spaß. Das füllt mich nich' aus, ich fühl' mich zu - haus nur zwi-schen den
F G C Am
Stühl'n. Ich will doch nur spiel'n. Hmm! Hmm!
F G C Am F
Ich tu' doch nichts. Ich
G C Am F G
will doch nur spiel'n. Hmm! Hmm! Ich
1.
C Am F G
tu' doch nichts. 2.Dass du we-gen

2.
C Am F G C
tu' doch nichts.
Am F G C Am
F G C Am F G
C Am F G
D.S.al
3.Dass du nich' mehr
C Am F G
tu' doch nichts.
Ich tu' doch nichts.
C Am F G C
Am F G C Am
Ich will doch nur spiel'n.
F G C Am
Ich tu' doch nichts.
Ich
F G C
tu' doch nichts.
rit.

DEATH OF A CLOWN

♩	164	Foxtrot

1.
C G7
My makeup is dry and it cracks on my chin,
F C G G7
I'm drowning my sorrows in whisky and gin.
C G7
The lion tamer's whip doesn't crack any more,
F C G G7
the lions, they won't fight and the tigers won't roar.

Ref.
F Dm B♭ E♭
La la la la, la la la la la la,
Dm C G7
so let's go and drink to the death of a clown.
C G7
Won't someone help me to break up his crown,
F C G7
let's all drink to the death of a clown.
F Dm B♭ E♭
La la la la, la la la la la la,
Dm C G G7
let's all drink to the death of a clown.

2.
C G7
The old fortune teller lies dead on the floor,
F C G G7
nobody needs fortunes told anymore.
C G7
The trainer of insects is crouched on his knees
F C G G7
and furtively looking for runaway fleas.

Ref. La la la la, ...

3.
C G7 F C G G7 C G7 F C G G7
La la la, ...

Ref. La la la la, ... *(fade out)*

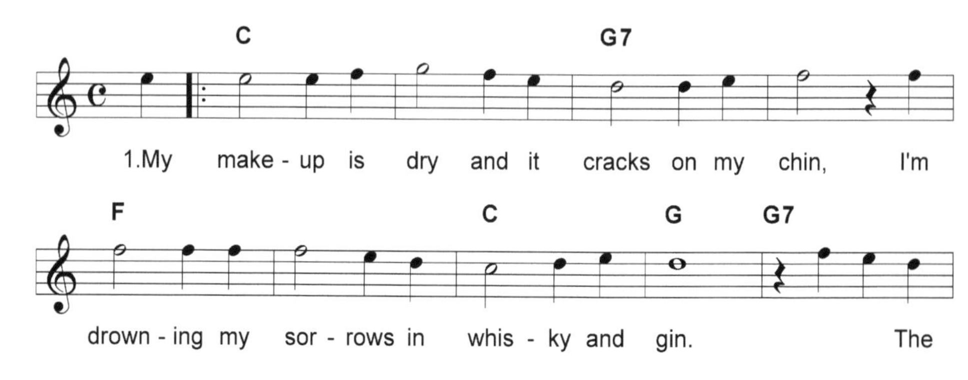

C G7
lion ta-mer's whip does-n't crack a - ny more, the
F C G G7
lions, they won't fight and the ti - gers won't roar.
F Dm B♭ E♭
La la la la, la la la la la la, so
Dm C G7
let's go and drink to the death of a clown.
C G7 F
Won't some-one help me to break up his crown, let's all
C G7 F
drink to the death of a clown. La la la la,
Dm B♭ E♭ Dm
la la la la la la, let's all
C G G7
drink to the death of a clown. 2.The

DETROIT CITY

♩ 117 | Country-Shuffle

```
        D       A7          D       D7                  G
Ref.        I wanna go home!       I wanna go home!
        D           A7          D
        Oh, how I wanna go home!

               D                 A                  D
1.      Last night I went to sleep in Detroit City
                 A                          A7                  D      D7
        and I dreamed about those cotton fields and home.
          G                                          D
        I dreamed about my mother, dear old pappa, sister and brother,
          E7                                         A              A7
        I dreamed about the girl who's been waitin' there so long.

          (A7)          D       D7                   G
Ref.    I wanna go home!       I wanna go home!
        D           A7          D
        Oh, how I wanna go home!

             D                       A               D
2.      My kinfolks think I'm big in Detroit City.
                   A                A7                  D   D7
        From the letters that I write they think I'm fine.
            G                           D
        By day I make the cars, by night I make the bars,
          E7                                       A     A7
        if only they could read between the lines.

        D                                    A            D
3.      (gespr.:) 'cause you know       I rode a freight train north to Detroit City
             A                              A7                   D              D7
        and after all these years I find I've just been wastin' my time.
              G
        You know what I'm gonna do? I'm gonna take my foolish pride,
                          D
        get it on a southbound freight and let it ride.
        E7                                                               A                   A7
            I'm gonna go back to the loved ones, the ones I left waiting so far behind!

Ref.    I wanna go home! ...
```

Words & Music by Danny Dill & Mel Tillis

N.C.
D A7 D
I wan-na go home!
D7 G D A7
I wan-na go home! Oh, how I wan - na go
D D A D
home! 1.Last night I went to sleep in De-troit Ci-ty
A A7 D
and I dreamed a-bout those cot-ton fields and home.
D7 G
I dreamed a-bout my moth-er, dear old
D E7
pap-pa, sis - ter and bro-ther, I dreamed a-bout the
A A7
girl who's been wait-in' there so long. I wan-na go
D.S.

DON'T LET ME BE MISUNDERSTOOD

♩	118	Disco

```
Intro  //: Am   G   F   E   ://

   Am                       G
Baby, do you understand me now,
F                        E
   sometimes I feel a little mad,
      Am                                    G
but don't you know that no-one-alive can always be an angel.
F                              E
   When things go wrong I seem to be bad.
         C                  Em     Am              G
'Cause I'm just a soul whose intentions are good.
F                                               Am   G   F   E
   Oh! Lord, please don't let me be misunderstood.
F        G        F        G
If I seem edgy, I want you to know,
  F           G          C       Am
that I never mean to take it out on you.
 F          G           F       G
Life has its problems, and I get my share,
  F                G            C             E7
that's one thing I never mean to do, 'cause I love you.
Am                      G
     Baby, don't you know I'm just human,
F                          E
   and I've got thougts like any other one.
       Am                              G
And sometimes I feel myself, oh Lord, regretting,
F                              E
   some foolish thing, some foolish thing I've done.
         C                  Em     Am              G
'Cause I'm just a soul whose intentions are good.
F                                               Am
   Oh! Lord, please don't let me be misunderstood.

Outro  //: Am   G   F   E   :// Wdhl. & Improvisation ad lib., dann fade out
```

Words & Music by Bennie Benjamin, Gloria Caldwell & Sol Marcus

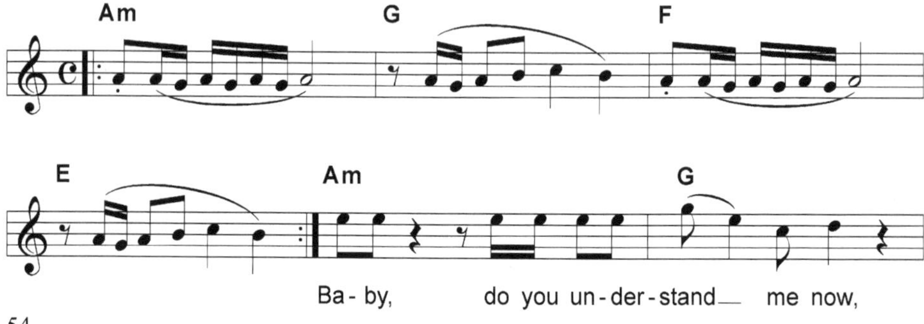

F
E
some - times I feel a lit - tle mad, but
Am
G
don't you know that no-one-a-live can al - ways be an an - gel.
F
E
When things go wrong I seem to be bad. 'Cause
C
Em
Am
G
F
I'm just a soul whose in - ten - tions are good. Oh! Lord,
Am
please don't let me be mis - un - der - stood.
G
F
E
F
G
F
G
If I seem edg - y, I want you to know,
F
G
C
Am
that I ne - ver mean to take it out on you.
F
G
F
G
Life has its pro - blems, and I get my share,

F G C E7
that's one thing I ne - ver mean to do, 'cause I love you.
Am G F
3 3
Ba - by, don't you know I'm just hu - man, and I've got thougts like
E Am
3
a - ny oth - er one.
And some - times I feel my - self, oh
G F
Lord, re - gret - ting, some fool - ish thing, some
E C Em
fool - ish thing I've done. 'Cause I'm just a soul whose in -
Am G F
ten - tions are good. Oh! Lord,
Am
please don't let me be mis - un - der - (stood.)
G F E
Wdhl. & Improvisation ad lib., dann fade out

DON'T LOOK BACK IN ANGER

♩	82	Rock-Ballad

```
      C              G              Am                E7              F
1.    Slip inside the eye of your mind, don't you know you might find
      G                      C   Am G
        a better place to play.
       C             G              Am                E7                F
      You said that you'd never been, but all the things that you've seen
      G                  C    Am G
        sort of fade away.

      F                    Fm                 C
Br.     So I start a revolution from my bed,
                F                  Fm                C
      'cos you said the brains I had went to my head.
        F                 Fm               C
      Step outside the summertime's in bloom.
        G                                  E7/G#
      Stand up beside the fireplace, take that look from off your face,
           Am               G                 F          G
      'cos you ain't ever gonna burn my heart out. ----

           C  G          Am            E7            F               G           C  Am G
Ref.  And so Sally can wait, she knows it's too late as we're walking on by.
          C    G         Am  E7                 F                 G                 C
      Her soul slides away,       but don't look back in anger      I heard you say.

Zw.   (C) G Am E7 F G C Am G

       C                  G                   Am         E7        F
2.    Take me to the place where you go, where nobody knows
      G                    C   Am G
        if it's night or day.
        C                      G            Am          E7            F
      Please don't put your life in the hands of a Rock'n Roll band
      G                            C   Am G
        who'll throw it all away.                     Br. ...   Ref. ...

           C  G          Am            E7            F               G           C  Am G
Ref.  And so Sally can wait, she knows it's too late as we're walking on by.
          C    G         Am  E7                 F                 G                 C   Am G
      My soul slides away,       but don't look back in anger      I heard you say.

           C  G          Am            E7            F               G           C  Am G
Ref.  And so Sally can wait, she knows it's too late as she's walking on by.
          C    G         Am   E7                F
      My soul slides away,        but don't look back in anger,
                     Fm                           C    G E7 Am E7 F
      don't look back in anger,  I heard you say
      Fm            C
          at least not today.
```

Words & Music by Noel Gallagher

C G Am E7
1.Slip in-side the eye of your mind, don't you know you might find
F G C Am G
a bet-ter place to play.
C G Am E7
You said that you'd ne - ver been, but all the things that you've seen
F G C Am G
sort of fade a - way.
F Fm C
So I start a re - vo - lu - tion from my bed, 'cos you
F Fm C
said the brains I had went to my head.
F Fm C
Step out - side the sum-mer - time's in bloom.
G E7/G♯
Stand up be - side the fi - re - place, take that look from off your face, 'cos
Am G F G
you ain't e - ver gon-na burn my heart out.

C G Am E7
And so Sal-ly can wait, she knows it's too late
F G C Am G C G
as we're walk - ing on by. Her soul slides a-way,
Am E7 F G C G
but don't look back in an - ger I heard you say.
Am E7 F G C Am G
D.C.al Coda
C Am G
say. And
C G Am E7
so Sal - ly can wait, she knows it's too late
F G C Am G C G
as she's walk - ing on by. My soul slides a-way,
Am E7 F
Frei im Tempo
but don't look back in an - ger, don't look
Fm C G E7
back in an ger, I heard you say
Am E7 F Fm C
at least not to - day.

DON'T WORRY BE HAPPY

𝅗𝅥	68	Reggae

C   **Dm**   **F**
Ref. Uh! Uh! Uh! ...   Don't worry. Uh! Uh! Uh! ... Be happy.
              C   **F**   **C**   **F**
Uh! Uh! Uh! ... Don't worry, be happy.
C   **Dm**   **F**
Uh! Uh! Uh! ...   Don't worry. Uh! Uh! Uh! ... Be happy.
              C   **F**   **C**   **F**
Uh! Uh! Uh! ... Don't worry, be happy.

C   **Dm**
1.   Here's a little song I wrote, you might want to sing it note for note.
          F   **C**   **F** **C** **F**
Don't worry, be happy.
C   **Dm**
   In every life we have some trouble   but when you worry you make it doubl
          F   **C**   **F**   **C**   **F**
Don't worry, be happy.   Don't worry, be happy now.

Ref. Uh! Uh! Uh! ...

C   **Dm**
2.   Ain't got no place to lay your head,   somebody came and took your bed.
          F   **C**   **F** **C** **F**
Don't worry, be happy.
     C   **Dm**
The landlord say your rent is late,   he may have to litigate.
          F   **C**   **F**   **C**   **F**
Don't worry, be happy.   Look at me, I am happy.

Ref. Uh! Uh! Uh! ...

C   **Dm**
3.   Ain't got no cash, ain't got no style,   ain't got no gal to make you smile.
              F   **C**   **F** **C** **F**
But don't worry be happy.
          C   **Dm**
'Cause when you worry your face will frown, and that will bring everybody down
          F   **C**   **F**   **C**   **F**
Don't worry, be happy.   Don't worry, be happy now.

Ref. Uh! Uh! Uh! ...   *(3x, fade out)*

C
Dm
Uh! Uh! Uh! Don't
F
wor - ry. Uh! Uh! Uh! Be hap - py. Uh! Uh!
C F C F C
Uh! Don't wor - ry, be hap - py. 1.Here's a lit - tle
Dm
song I wrote, you might want to sing it note for note. Don't
F C F C F
wor - ry, be hap - py.
C
In eve - ry life we have some trou - ble
Dm
but when you wor - ry you make it dou - ble. Don't
F C F
wor - ry, be hap - py. Don't
C F D.C.
wor - ry, be hap - py now.

DOWN ON THE CORNER

♩	108	Pop-Reggae

Intro C G C G C F C G C

1.
C G C
Early in the evenin' just about supper time,
G C
over by the courthouse they're standing to unwind.
F C
Four kids on the corner trying to bring you up.
G C
Willy picks a tune out and he blows it on the harp.

Ref.
F C G C
Down on the corner, out in the street,
F C G C
Willy and the Poorboys are playin'; bring a nickel; tap your feet.

2.
C G C
Rooster hits the washboard and people just got to smile,
G C
Blinky thumps the gut bass and solos for a while.
F C
Poorboy twangs the rhythm out on his kalomazoo.
G C
Willy goes into a dance and doubles on kazoo.

Ref. Down on the corner, ...

Intro C G C G C F C G C

Ref. Down on the corner, ...

Zw. C G C G C

3.
C G C
You don't need a penny just to hang around,
G C
but if you've got a nickel, won't you lay your money down?
F C
Over the corner there's a happy noise.
G C
People come from all around to watch the magic boys.

Ref. Down on the corner, ... *(wdhl. nach Belieben, fade out)*

Words & Music by John C Fogerty

C
G
C
F
C
G
C
C
G
1.Ear - ly in the eve - nin' just a - bout sup - per time,
C
G
o - ver by the court - house they're stand - ing to un - wind.
C
F
C
Four kids on the cor - ner try - ing to bring you up.
Wil - ly picks a tune out and he
G
C
F
C
blows it on the harp. Down on the cor - ner,
G
C
F
out in the street, Wil - ly and the Poor - boys are play -
C
G
C
- in'; bring a nick - el; tap your feet.
D.S.

DREAMER

♩	80	8 Ballad

```
    C                              Am
1.  Gazing through the window at the world outside,
     C                         Am
    wondering will mother earth survive.
     F                          Dm            G    G4  G
    Hoping that mankind will stop abusing her sometime.

    C                     Am
2.  After all there's only just a two of us
         C                           Am
    and here we are still fighting for our lives.
     F                   Dm              G    G4  G
    Watching all of history repeat itself time after time.

                 C         Am          Em  G
Ref. I'm just a dreamer, I dream my life away.
                 C            Am          Em   G
    I'm just a dreamer, who dreams of better days.

      C                              Am
3.  I watch the sun go down like every one of us.
       C                            Am
    I'm hoping that the dawn will bring a sign.
      F                                Dm            G    G4  G
    A better place for those who will come after us this time.       Ref. ...

        Dm                          G
Zw. Your higher power may be God or Jesus Christ.
      Dm                          G
    It doesn't really matter much to me.
       Dm                                G
    Without each other's help there ain't no hope for us.
       Dm                    G                C
    I'm living in a dream, a fantasy. Oh, yeah, yeah, yeah!

Br. (C) Am  C  Am  C  Am  Em  G  C  C/B♭  C/A  C/A♭  C  C/B♭  C/A  C/A♭

     C                            Am
4.  If only we could all just find serenity,
      C                              Am
    it would be nice if we could live as well.
      F                              Dm        G    G4  G
    When will all this anger, hate and bigotry be gone?

                 C         Am          Em    G
Ref. I'm just a dreamer, I dream my life away today.
                 C            Am           Em        G
    I'm just a dreamer, who dreams of better days. Oh, yeah!
                 C            Am               Em   G
    I'm just a dreamer, who's searching for the way today.
                 C         Am             Em
    I'm just a dreamer, dreaming my life away.
        G            C    C/B♭  C/A  C/A♭  C  C/B♭  C/A  C
    Oh, yeah, yeah, yeah!
```

C
Am
1.Gaz-ing through the win - dow at the world out-side,
C
Am
won - der-ing will mo-ther earth sur - vive.
F
Dm
Hop-ing that man-kind will stop a-bus - ing her some-time.
G
1.G4 G
2.G4 G
C
I'm just a drea-mer, I
Am
Em
G
dream my life a - way.
I'm just a
C
Am
Em
drea - mer, who dreams of bet - ter days.
G D.C.al 1(o. Wdhlg.)
G
Dm
3.I
Your high-er po-wer may be God or
G
Dm
Je-sus Christ. It does-n't real-ly mat-ter much to
G
Dm
me. With-out each o-ther's help there ain't no

G Dm
hope for __ us. I'm liv-ing in a dream, a fan - ta -
G C Am
sy. __ Oh, yeah, yeah, yeah!
C Am C
Am Em G C C/B♭
C/A C/A♭ C C/B♭ C/A C/A♭ D.C.al 𝄌2 (o. Wdh
4.If
𝄌2 Am Em G
dreams of bet - ter __ days. __ Oh, yeah! __ I'm just a
C Am Em
drea - mer, __ who search-ing for __ the __ way __ to - day.
G C Am
__ I'm just a drea - mer, __ dream - ing my life a - way. __
Em G C C/B♭ C/A C/A♭
__ Oh, yeah, yeah, yeah!
C C/B♭ C/A C
rit.

DUST IN THE WIND

♩	94	Folk (Rock)

```
       C    G Am  G            Dm              Am             G
1.     I close my eyes only for a moment and the moment's gone.
       C   G   Am    G                 Dm      Am
       All my dreams, pass before my eyes a curiosity.

       D          G           Am   C  D            G          Am   (G)
Ref.     Dust --  in the wind,        all we are is dust in the wind.

        C    G    Am  G                Dm       Am            G
2.     Same old song, just a drop of water in an endless sea.
       C   G Am  G                 Dm                  Am
       All we do crumbles to the ground, though we refuse to see.

Ref.   Dust in the wind, ...

        C     G   Am  G                Dm         Am              G
3.     Don't hang on nothing lasts forever but the earth and sky,
          C   G Am      G                  Dm         Am
       it slips away and all your money won't another minute buy.

Ref.   Dust in the wind, ...
```

EASY LIVIN'

♩ 160 | Rock Shuffle

1.
```
Dm                                                  F      Dm
This is a thing I've never known before, it's called easy livin'.
                                                  F      Dm
This is a place I've never seen before, and I've been forgiven.
```

Ref.
```
G    Dm            G       Dm
Easy livin' and I've been forgiven
           G          F          Dm
since you've   taken your place in my heart.
```

2.
```
Dm                                         F      Dm
Somewhere along the lonely road I had tried to find you.
                                            p F       Dm
Day after day on that winding road I had walked behind you.
```

Ref. Easy livin' ...

Br.
```
Am F     Am F     Am           G          Am
Waiting, watching, wishing my whole life away.
 Bm G     Bm G     Am        G        F
Dreaming, thinking, ready for my happy day
                Dm
and some easy livin'.
```

2.
```
Dm                                         F      Dm
Somewhere along the lonely road I had tried to find you.
                                           F       Dm
Day after day on that windy road I had walked behind you.
```

Ref. Easy livin' ...

Ref. Easy livin' ...

Outro **(Dm) A G F Em A Dm**

Words and Music by Ken Hensley

FERRY 'CROSS THE MERSEY

♩	103	Rhumba-Beat

```
        C   Gm C             Gm          C  Gm C Gm
1.      Life         goes on day after day,
          C     Gm C              Gm     C  Gm C Gm
        hearts            torn in ev'ry way.
           C                 Em              Dm               G
        So ferry 'cross the Mersey 'cos this land's the place I love
                        C   Gm C Gm
        and here I'll stay.

          C  Gm C              Gm            C  Gm C Gm
2.      Peo --------ple they rush ev'rywhere,
        C    Gm C                 Gm             C  Gm C Gm
        each          with their own secret care.
           C                 Em         Dm                G
        So ferry 'cross the Mersey and always take me there
                      C
        the place I love.

          Dm     G7           C
Zw.:    People around ev'ry corner,
        Dm                    G7        C
            they seem to smile and say,
        Dm             G7              Em
            we don't care what your name is boy,
          D7                       G7
        we'll never turn you away.

          C  Gm C          Gm       C  Gm C Gm
3.      So            I'll continue to say,
          C    Gm C   Gm            C  Gm C Gm
        here           I always will stay.
           C                 Em              Dm               G
        So ferry 'cross the Mersey 'cos this land's the place I love
                        C   Gm C Gm
        and here I'll stay,
        C       Gm      C   Gm  C   Gm       C   Gm  C  Gm  C
           and here I'll stay,            here I'll stay.
```

C Gm C Gm C Gm C Gm
Life goes on day af - ter day,
C Gm C Gm C Gm C Gm
hearts torn in ev - 'ry way. So
C Em Dm
fer - ry 'cross the Mer - sey 'cos this land's the place I
G 1. C Gm C Gm
love and here I'll stay.
2. C Dm G7 C
love. Peo-ple a - round ev - 'ry cor - ner,
Dm G7 C Dm G7
they seem to smile and say, we don't care what your
Em D7 G7
name is boy, we'll nev-er turn you a - way.
D.C.al Coda
C Gm C Gm C Gm C Gm
stay, and here I'll stay, here I'll
C Gm C Gm C
stay.

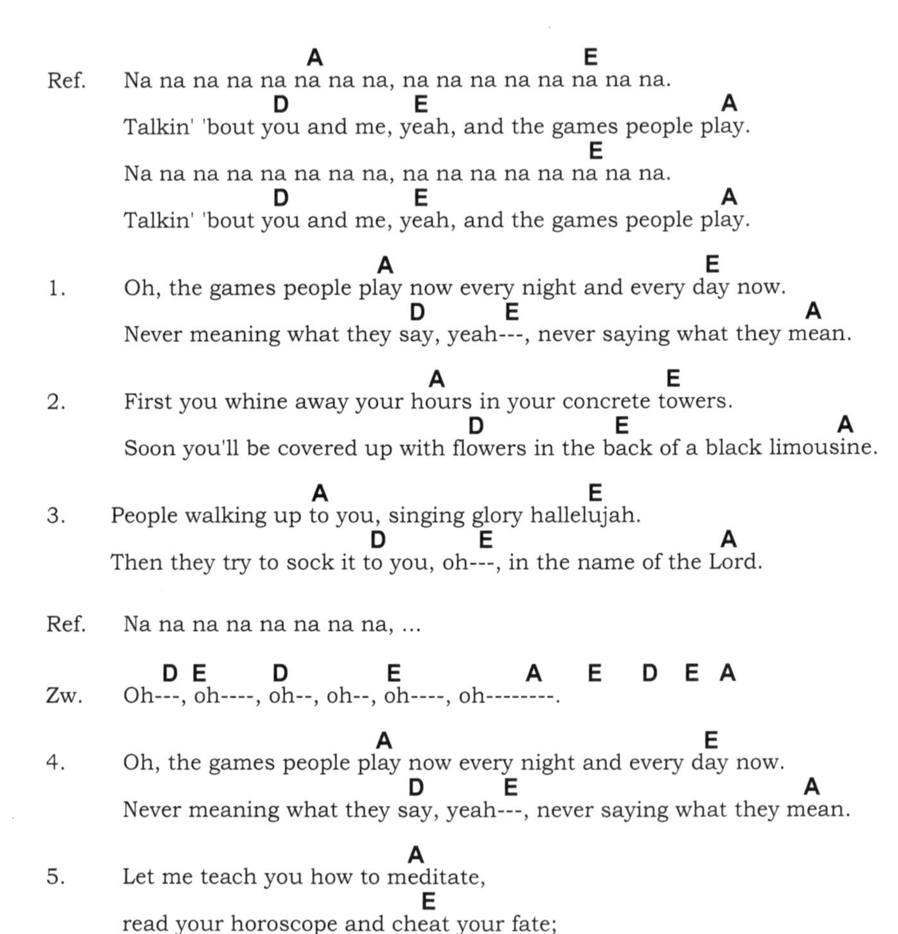

GAMES PEOPLE PLAY

𝅗𝅥	85	Reggae

Ref.
A E
Na na na na na na na na, na na na na na na na na.
D E A
Talkin' 'bout you and me, yeah, and the games people play.
E
Na na na na na na na na, na na na na na na na na.
D E A
Talkin' 'bout you and me, yeah, and the games people play.

1.
A E
Oh, the games people play now every night and every day now.
D E A
Never meaning what they say, yeah---, never saying what they mean.

2.
A E
First you whine away your hours in your concrete towers.
D E A
Soon you'll be covered up with flowers in the back of a black limousine.

3.
A E
People walking up to you, singing glory hallelujah.
D E A
Then they try to sock it to you, oh---, in the name of the Lord.

Ref. Na na na na na na na na, ...

Zw.
D E D E A E D E A
Oh---, oh----, oh--, oh--, oh----, oh--------.

4.
A E
Oh, the games people play now every night and every day now.
D E A
Never meaning what they say, yeah---, never saying what they mean.

5.
A
Let me teach you how to meditate,
E
read your horoscope and cheat your fate;
D
and furthermore to hell with hate,
E A
come on and gimme some more, more, more.

Ref. Na na na na na na na na, ...

Br.
A E
'Cos you're givin' up your sanity, turn your back on humanity,
D E A
yeah, and you don't give a damn, a damn, a damn.

Zw.
D E D E
Oh---, oh----, oh--, oh--, oh----.

Ref. Na na na na na na na na, ... *(2x)*

A Talkin' 'bout you and me, yeah, and the games people play. (chords: A, D, E, A)
Oh, talkin' 'bout you and me, yeah, and the games people play. (chords: D, E, A)

3. A
2.First you whine a - way your (3.)Lord.
A
Na na na na na na na na, na na na na na
E D
na na na. Talk - in' 'bout you and me, yeah,
E 1&2 1. A
and the games peo - ple play. Na na na na na
2. A D
play. Oh, oh,
E D
oh, oh,
E
oh, oh.
A E D
E A D.S.al 1
4.Oh, the games peo - ple

A
A
play.
'Cos you're giv - in' up your sa - ni - ty,
E
D
turn your back on hu - man - i - ty,
yeah,
E
A
and you don't give a damn, a damn, a damn.
Oh,
D
E
oh,
oh,
D
E
oh,
oh.
D.S.al 2
Na na na na na
A
play.
A
D
E
Talk - in' 'bout you and me, yeah, and the games peo - ple
1. A
2. A
play.
play.

GET BACK

♩ 123 Rock-Beat

```
        G
1.      Jo Jo was a man who thought he was a loner,
         C                      G
        but he knew it couldn't last.

        Jo Jo left his home in Tucson, Arizona,
        C                     G
        for some California grass.

           G7                     C7                   G
Ref.    Get back! Get back! Get back to where you once belonged.
        F  C  G7                    C7                   G
          Get back! Get back! Get back to where you once belonged.

        (Solo) G     C7   G F C G     C7   G

        F  C  G7                    C7                   G
          Get back! Get back! Get back to where you once belonged.
        F  C  G7                    C
          Get back! Get back! Get back to where you once belonged.

           G
2.      Sweet Loretta Martin thought she was a woman,
         C                       G
        but she was another man.

        All the girls around her say she's got it coming,
         C                         G
        but she gets it while she can.

Ref.    Get back! Get back! ...

        G
Ref.    (gespr.:) Get back Loretta,
        C7                 G          F C
          your mama's waitin' for ya!
        G
          Wearin' her high-heel shoes and a low-neck sweater.
        C7                    G
          Get back home, Loretta!

        F  C  G7
Ref.      Get back! Get back! ...  (fade out)
```

C
- son, A - ri - zo - na, for some Ca - li - for - nia grass.
G G7
Get back! Get back! Get back
C7 G F C G7
to where you once be - longed, Get back! Get back!
C7 G
Get back to where you once be - longed.
G C7
G F C G
C7 G F C G7
Get back! Get back!
C7
Get back to where you once be - longed.
G F C G7
Get back! Get back! Get back
C
D.C.
to where you once be - longed.

GROOVY KIND OF LOVE

♩	72	16 Ballad

Intro **G D/G G D/G**

1.
G D/G
When I'm feelin' blue, all I have to do
G Am/G
is take a look at you, then I'm not so blue.
Am Bm
When you're close to me, I can feel your heartbeat,
C D
I can hear you breathing in my ear.
G D/G G D
Wouldn't you agree, baby, you and me got a groovy kind of love.

2.
G D/G
Anytime you want to, you can turn me on to
G Am/G
anything you want to, anytime at all.
Am Bm
When I kiss your lips, uh, I start to shiver,
C D
can't control the quivering inside.
G D/G G D/G G D/G
Wouldn't you agree, baby, you and me got a groovy kind of love.

3.
G D/G
When I'm feelin' blue, all I have to do
G Am/G
is take a look at you, then I'm not so blue.
Am Bm
When I'm in your arms, nothing seems to matter,
C D
my whole world could shatter, I don't care.
G D/G G
Wouldn't you agree, baby, you and me got a groovy kind of love.
D/G G
We got a groovy kind of love.
D/G C/E D4 C/E D4 C/E
We got a groovy kind of love.
D4 D G
We got a groovy kind of love.

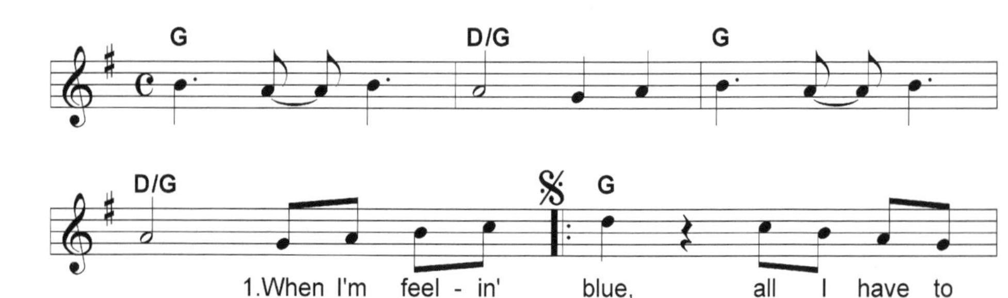

D/G G
do is take a look at you, then I'm not so
Am/G Am
blue. When you're close to me, I can feel your
Bm C D
heart - beat, I can hear you breath - ing in my ear. Would - n't you a
G D/G 1. G
gree, ba - by, you and me got a groo - vy kind of love.
D 2. G D/G G
2.A-ny - time you
D/G
3.When I'm feel - in'
D.S.al Coda
G
love.
D/G G
We got a groo - vy kind of love.
D/G C/E Dsus4
We got a groo-vy kind of love.
C/E Dsus4 C/E
Dsus4 D G
We got a groo - vy kind of love.

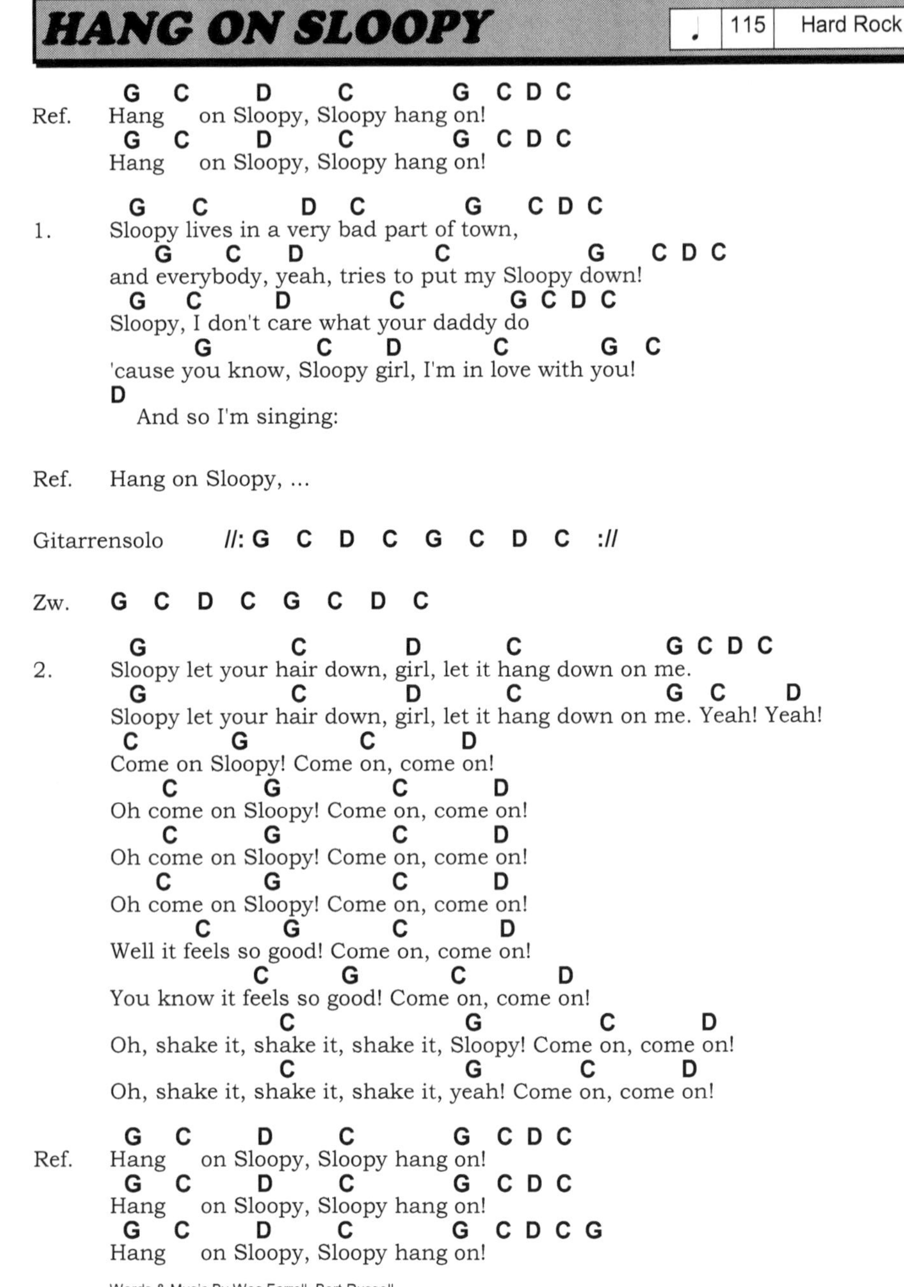

HANG ON SLOOPY

♩	115	Hard Rock

```
         G   C      D      C          G  C D C
Ref.     Hang    on Sloopy, Sloopy hang on!
         G   C      D      C          G  C D C
         Hang    on Sloopy, Sloopy hang on!

          G    C        D   C           G    C D C
1.       Sloopy lives in a very bad part of town,
            G    C    D          C              G    C D C
         and everybody, yeah, tries to put my Sloopy down!
          G   C     D         C           G C D C
         Sloopy, I don't care what your daddy do
                 G         C    D        C          G   C
         'cause you know, Sloopy girl, I'm in love with you!
         D
           And so I'm singing:

Ref.     Hang on Sloopy, ...

Gitarrensolo    //: G  C  D  C  G  C  D  C  ://

Zw.      G  C  D  C  G  C  D  C

          G                C          D         C                G C D C
2.       Sloopy let your hair down, girl, let it hang down on me.
          G                C          D         C                G  C     D
         Sloopy let your hair down, girl, let it hang down on me. Yeah! Yeah!
          C        G         C        D
         Come on Sloopy! Come on, come on!
             C       G         C        D
         Oh come on Sloopy! Come on, come on!
             C       G         C        D
         Oh come on Sloopy! Come on, come on!
            C        G         C        D
         Oh come on Sloopy! Come on, come on!
                C     G         C        D
         Well it feels so good! Come on, come on!
                     C     G         C        D
         You know it feels so good! Come on, come on!
                         C               G          C         D
         Oh, shake it, shake it, shake it, Sloopy! Come on, come on!
                         C              G          C         D
         Oh, shake it, shake it, shake it, yeah! Come on, come on!

          G   C      D      C          G  C D C
Ref.     Hang    on Sloopy, Sloopy hang on!
          G   C      D      C          G  C D C
         Hang    on Sloopy, Sloopy hang on!
          G   C      D      C          G  C D C G
         Hang    on Sloopy, Sloopy hang on!
```

Words & Music By Wes Farrell, Bert Russell

G C D C G C
Hang on Sloo-py, Sloo-py hang on!
D C G C D C
1.Sloo-py lives in a ve-ry bad part of
G C D C G C
town, and eve-ry-bo-dy, yeah,
D C G C D C
tries to put my Sloo-py down!
G C D C G C
3
Sloo-py, I don't care what your dad-dy do
D C G C D C
'cause you know, Sloo-py girl, I'm in love with
G C D G C
you! And so I'm sing-ing: Hang on
D C G C D C
Sloo-py, Sloo-py hang on!

G C D C
3
2.Sloo-py let your hair down, girl,
let it hang down on
G C D C G C
me.
Sloo-py let your hair down, girl,
D C G C D C
3
let it hang down on me. Yeah! Yeah! Come on
G C D C
Sloo - py! Come on, come on! Oh come on
G C D C
Sloo - py! Come on, come on! Oh come on
G C D C
Sloo - py! Come on, come on! Oh come on
G C D C
Sloo - py! Come on, come on! Well it feels so
G C D C
good! Come on, come on! You know it feels so

G C D C
good! Come on, come on! Oh, shake it, shake it, shake it,
G C D C
Sloo-py! Come on, come on! Oh, shake it, shake it, shake it,
G C D G C
yeah! Come on, come on! Hang on
D C G C D C
Sloo-py, Sloo-py hang on!
G C D C G C
Hang on Sloo-py, Sloo-py hang on!
D C G

HE AIN'T HEAVY HE'S MY BROTHER

♩	77	8 Ballad

```
                  G    D/F#                 C/E
1.     The road is long        with many a winding turn,
       Am         D          D#0     Em            F                   Am   D2  D
           that leads us       to who knows where, who knows where.
                          G    D/F#                Em    Eb
       But I'm strong, strong          enough to carry him.

       G                      Am  D4            G
Ref.      He ain't heavy,               he's my brother.

       Am        D        G  D/F#                      C/E
2.          So on we go          his welfare is of my concern,
       Am        D        D#0      Em   F                Am   D2  D
            no burden          is he to bear, we'll get there.
               G   D/F#                     Em       Eb
       For I know        he would not encumber me.          Ref. ...

       Am  G7/B           C         D/C      C           D/C
Zw.                 If I'm laden at all, I'm laden with sadness,
           Bm/D                     C      B7          Em G/D
       that everyone's heart isn't filled       with the gladness
          C   C/B A7               D4     D
       of love ---------  for one another.

                           G   D/F#                     C/E
3.     It's a long long road         from which there is no return,
       Am     D  D#0                   Em      F              Am   D2  D
           while       we're on the way to there, why not share.
                G   D/F#                        Em     Eb
       And the load        doesn't weigh me down at all.     Ref. ...

Zw.    (G)  D/F#  C/E  Am  D D#0 Em  F  Am  D2

                      G       D/F# Em  D2               G    D/F#
       //: He's my brother.                He ain't heavy. ---- ://  (fade out)
```

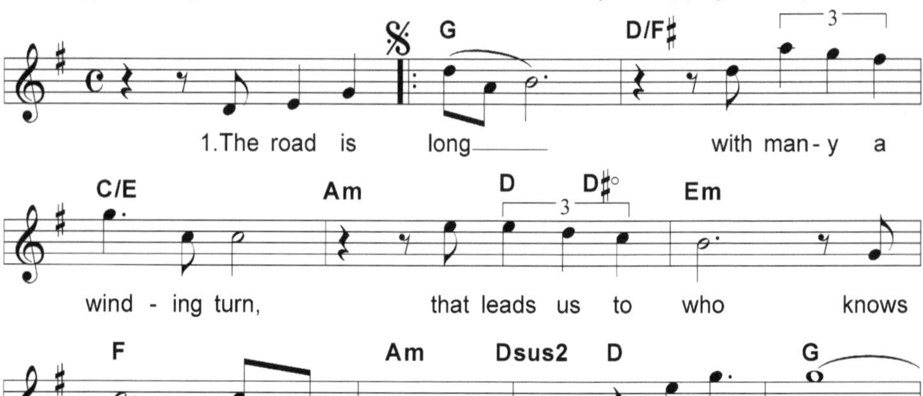

D/F♯ Em E♭ G
strong e - nough to car - ry him. He ain't hea - vy,
Am Dsus4 1. G Am D 2. G
he's my broth - er. 2.So on we broth - er.
Am G7/B C D/C
If I'm lad - en at all, I'm
C D/C Bm/D
lad - en with sad - ness, that eve - ry - one's
C B7 Em G/D C C/B
heart is-n't filled with the glad - ness of love
A7 Dsus4 D
for one a - noth - er. 3.It's a long long
D.S.al Φ
G D/F♯ C/E Am D D♯°
broth - er.
Em F Am Dsus2 G
He's my broth - er.
D/F♯ Em Dsus2 G D/F♯
fade out
He ain't hea - vy. He's my

I DON'T LIKE MONDAYS

𝅗𝅥	72	Ballad

```
           C                 Em
1.      The silicon chip inside her head
              F                  G    F G
        gets switched to overload,
            C                           Em
        and nobody's gonna go to school today,
                       F                 G
        she's gonna make them stay at home.
            F                         G4     G              C                G        F
        And Daddy doesn't understand it,      he always said she was as good as gold,

        and he can see no reason, cause there are no reasons.
                                                 G      G7
        What reason do you need to be sho – o – o – o - own?

                      C                Em/B
Ref.    Tell me why I don't like Mondays,
                     F/A               G   F
        tell me why I don't like Mondays.
          G          C                Em/B
        Tell me why I don't like Mondays,
                       F          G                      C     (Em   F   G  F )
        I wanna shoot---------- the whole day down.

           C                     Em
2.      The telex machine is kept so clean
              F                     G     F G
        and it types to a waiting world.
                          C                           Em
        And mother feels so shocked, father's world is rocked,
                         F                 G
        and their thoughts turn to their own little girl.
           F                         G4     G         C         G           F
        Sweet sixteen ain't that peachy keen, no it ain't so neat to admit defeat.

        They can see no reasons, cause there are no reasons.
                                                 G      G7
        What reason do you need to be sho – o – o – o - own?


Ref.    Tell me why I don't like Mondays, ...

                         F          G                     E4
        ... I wanna shoot---------- the whole day down,
          Em     E4     Em         C     C4 C   E4  Em  E4  Em  F   G   C
        down, down, shoot it all down.

                          C                          Em
3.      And all the playing's stopped in the playground now,
             F                       G
        she wants to play with her toys a while.
                 C                     Em
        And school's out early and soon we'll be learning,
                   F              G
        and the lesson today is how to die.
```

F G4 G
And then the bullhorn crackles, and the captain tackles
C G F
with the problems and the how's and why's.

And he can see no reasons, cause there are no reasons.
G G7
What reason do you need to die, die, uuh-----?

C Em/B
Ref. Tell me why I don't like Mondays,
F/A G F
tell me why I don't like Mondays.
G C Em/B F/A G
Tell me why I don't like, I don't like, I don't like Mondays.
C Em F G
Tell me why I don't like, I don't like, I don't like Mondays.
C Em/B
Tell me why I don't like Mondays,
F G C
I wanna shoot---------- the whole day down.
Em F G C
Uuh! Uuh! Uuh! Uuh!

C G F
said she was good as gold, and he can
see no rea - son, cause there are no rea - sons. What
G G7
rea - son do you need to be shown? Tell me
C Em/B F/A
why I don't like Mon - days, tell me why I don't like
G F G C Em/B
Mon - days. Tell me why I don't like Mon - days, I wan - na
F G
shoot the whole day
C Em F
down.
G F
2.The D.S.al 1
G Esus4 Em
the whole day down, down,
Esus4 Em C Csus4 C Esus4 Em
down, shoot it all down.

Esus4 Em F G C
D.S.al 𝄌2
3.And all the
𝄌2 C
why I don't like
Em/B F/A G F G
Mon - days, tell me why I don't like Mon - days. Tell me
C Em/B F/A
why I don't like, I don't like, I don't like
G C Em
Mon - days. Tell me why I don't like, I don't like,
F G C
I don't like Mon - days. Tell me why I don't like
Em/B F G
Mon - days, I wan - na shoot
C Em
the whole day down. Uuh!
F G rit. C
Uuh! Uuh! Uuh!

HERE COMES THE SUN

♩ | 130 | 8 Beat

```
        G                          C                        A7
Ref.       Here comes the sun,        here comes the sun,
                      G                  C  G  Am  G  D
        and I say:     "It's all right!"

        G                               C                 D7
1.         Little darling, it's been a long, cold, lonely winter.
        G                                 C                   D7
           Little darling, it feels like years since it's been here.

        G                          C                        A7
Ref.       Here comes the sun,        here comes the sun,
                      G                  C  G  Am  G  D7
        and I say:     "It's all right!"

        G                                  C              D7
2.         Little darling, the smiles returning to their faces.
        G                                    C                   D7
           Little darling, it seems like years since it's been here.

        G                          C                        A7
Ref.       Here comes the sun,        here comes the sun,
                      G                  C  G  Am  G  D7
        and I say:     "It's all right!"

Zw.     (D7)  B♭  F  C   G

             D7  B♭   F   C              G             D7
Br.     //:      Sun, sun, sun, here it comes. ://
                                            (4x wdhl.)

        G                              C             D7
3.         Little darling, I feel the ice is slowly melting.
        G                                    C                   D7
           Little darling, it seems like years since it's been clear.

        G                          C                        A7
Ref.       Here comes the sun,        here comes the sun,
                      G                  C  G  Am  G  D
        and I say:     "It's all right!"

        G                          C                        A7
Ref.       Here comes the sun,        here comes the sun,
        G                C  G  Am  G  D
           It's all right!
        G                C  G  Am  G  D  B♭  F  C   G
           It's all right!
```

Musik und Text: George Harrison

G
Here comes the sun,
C A7 G
here comes the sun, and I say: "It's all right!"
C G Am G D G
1.Lit - tle dar - ling,
C D7
it's been a long, cold, lone - ly win - ter.
G
Lit - tle dar - ling, it feels like years
C D7 G
since it's been here. Here comes the sun,
C A7
here comes the sun, and I say:
G C G Am G D
"It's all right!"

G
1.
D7
2.
D7
B♭
F
C
G
D7
B♭
F
C
G
4x wdhl.
Sun, sun, sun, here it comes.
D7
D.S.al
G
C
Here comes the sun, here comes the sun.
A7
G
C
G
Am
It's all right!
G
D
B♭
F
C
G
rit.

I FEEL LIKE BUDDY HOLLY

♩	114	8 Beat

```
Intro  G     C  D4 D G     C  D4 D G

       G                              C            G
1.        I watched the planes come in on the early morning flights,
           C        G      C      G      D
       but I could not stand to see them land without you.
                G                                C           A
       Now I'm thumbing through my forty-fives on another endless night,
               C        G     B7           Em  C          D         G
       and the same old lines going back in time, tell me this is nothing new.

             G   D   C                     Am          D
Ref.1. Well, I feel like Buddy Holly, 'cause it's raining in my heart.
            Am  D   G                         C               D
       All the sad songs take me back to you now that we are apart.
       C        G   D  C                        Am               D
         Now I know how Paul McCartney felt, when he got up to say:
        C G           D    G     C   D4 D G     C   D4 D G
       "I wish it was yesterday!"

           G                               C             G
2.     So I sit here playing Solitaire, it's a game I know so well.
           C         G      C      G     D
       Ever since that day you called to say it's over.
               G                          C          A
       Now I've made my reservation at the Heartbreak Hotel.
               C         G             B7       Em           C       D     G
       While I'm living without you, I'm thinking about you, like only the lonely do.

             G   D   C                     Am          D
Ref.2. Well, I feel like Buddy Holly, 'cause it's raining in my heart.
            Am  D   G                         C               D
       All the sad songs take me back to you now that we are apart.
       C         G      D C                    Am                D
          Now I know what Paul Simon meant       by the words he found:
        C G          D       G
       "I wish I was homeward bound!"

Ref.1. Well, I feel like Buddy Holly ...

          C      Am         D   G
       //:    "I wish it was yesterday!" :// (fade out)
```

Words & Music by Mike Batt

G C Dsus4 D
1. G 2. G G
1.I watched the planes
C G
come in on the ear - ly mor - ning flights, but I
C G C G
could not stand to see them land with -
D G
out you. Now I'm thumb - ing through my
C A
for - ty - fives on a - noth - er end - less night,
C G B7 Em
and the same old lines go - ing back in time,
C D G
tell me this is noth - ing new. Well, I

G D C Am
feel like Bud-dy Hol - ly, 'cause it's rain-ing in my heart.
D Am D G
All the sad songs take me back to you
C D C G D
now that we are a - part. Now I know how
C Am D C
Paul Mc-Cart - ney felt, when he got up to say: "I
G D G
wish it was yes - ter - day!"
D.S.al Coda
(mit Wdhl.)
G D G
wish it was yes - ter - day!"
C Am D G
fade out
"I wish it was yes - ter - day!"

I GOT YOU BABE

♩.	75	Slow Rock

```
              F                                   Bb
1.       They say we're young and we don't know,
              F                     Bb Eb        C
         we won't find out till---- we grow.
              F                      Bb                          F
         Well I don't know if all that's true, 'cause you got me,
                  Bb  Eb     C      F       Bb          F          Bb         F          Bb
         and baby, I got you, babe,       I got you babe,      I got you babe.

              F                                Bb
2.       They say our love won't pay the rent,
            F                              Bb     Eb          C
         before it's earned, our money's all been spent.
            F                                  Bb
         I guess that's so, we don't have a pot,
               F                           Bb       Eb        C
         but at least I'm sure of all the things we got,
          F    Bb           F           Bb          F
         babe,      I got you babe,      I got you babe.

              Gm                 C7
Zw.      I got flowers in the spring,
              Gm                 C7
         I got you, to wear my ring,
                             F             Bb
         and when I'm sad, you're a clown,
                                                C        C7
         and if I get scared, you're always around. ----

            F                          Bb
3.       So let them say your hair's too long,
               F                             Bb     Eb        C
         'cause I don't care, with you I can't go wrong.
               F                      Bb
         Then put your little hand in mine,
           F                             Bb     Eb          C
         there ain't no hill or mountain      we can't climb,
          F    Bb           F           Bb          F         Bb   F   Bb   F   C
         babe,      I got you babe,      I got you babe.

         F                Bb               F             C
Outro      I got you to hold my hand, I got you to understand.
         F                 Bb             F            C
           I got you to walk with me, I got you to talk with me.
         F                Bb                F           C
           I got you to kiss good night, I got you to hold me tight,
         F             Bb               F                  C             F   Bb   F   C
           I got you, I won't let go, I got you who loves me so.
            Bb F
          I got you Babe!
```

Words & Music by Sonny Bono

F Bb F
1.They say we're young and we don't know, we won't find out
Bb Eb C F
till we grow. Well I don't know if
Bb F Bb Eb C
all that's true, 'cause you got me, and ba-by, I got you,
F Bb F Bb
babe, I got you babe, I got
1. F Bb 2. F
you babe. 2.They you babe. I got
Gm C7
flo-wers in the spring, I got
Gm C7
you, to wear my ring, and when I'm
F Bb
sad, you're a clown, and if I get scared,

C
C7
D.S.al
you're al - ways a - round.
3.So
F
B♭
F
B♭
you babe.
F
C
F
B♭
I got you to hold my hand,
F
1.-4.
C
5.
C
B♭
F
I got you to un - der - stand.
I got you babe!
langsam

I JUST CALLED TO SAY I LOVE YOU

♩	114	Pop-Rhumba (8 Beat)

```
                      C
1.      No New Year's day to celebrate,
                                                     Dm  Dmj7
        no choclate covered candy hearts to give away.
                    Dm  Dmj7              Dm7  Dmj7
        No first of spring,      no song to sing
                    Dm           G7        C
        in fact here's just another ordinary day.

        No April rain, no flowers bloom,
                                                      Dm   Dmj7
        no wedding Saturday within the month of June.
                  Dm Dmj7                 Dm7  Dmj7
        But what it is,        is something true,
                    Dm                G7            C
        made up of these three words that I must say to you.

              Dm       G7   C              Dm       G               Am
Ref.    I just called to say I love you, I just called to say how much I care.
              Dm       G    Am             Dm                G7              C
        I just called to say I love you, and I mean it from the bottom of my heart.

                     C
2.      No summer's high, no warm July,
                                                       Dm   Dmj7
        no harvest moon to light one tender August night.
                     Dm  Dmj7              Dm7  Dmj7
        No autumn breeze,       no falling leaves,
                 Dm             G7             C
        not even time for birds to fly to southern skies.

        No Libra sun, no Halloween,
                                                          Dm   Dmj7
        no giving thanks to all the Christmas joy you bring.
                  Dm Dmj7                 Dm7  Dmj7
        But what it is,        though old so new,
                   Dm                 G7             C
        to fill your heart like no three words could ever do.


Ref.    I just called to say I love you, ...

Ref.    I just called to say I love you, ...

        Ab     Bb          C
        of my heart, of my heart.
```

Words & Music by Stevie Wonder

C
1.No New Year's day to ce - le - brate,
Dm
no choc-late cover-ed can - dy hearts to give a - way.
Dm(maj7) Dm Dm(maj7) Dm7
No first of spring, no song to sing
Dm(maj7) Dm G7
in fact here's just an-oth - er or - di-na - ry day.
C C
No A - pril rain, no flo - wers bloom.
Dm
no wed-ding Sa - tur-day with - in the month of June.
Dm(maj7) Dm Dm(maj7) Dm7
But what it is, is some-thing true,
Dm(maj7) Dm G7
made up of these three words that I must say to you.

C Dm G7
I just called to say I love
C Dm G
you, I just called to say how much I
Am Dm G
care. I just called to say I love
Am Dm G7
you, and I mean it from the bot-tom of my
1. C 2. C D.S.al Coda
heart. 2.No sum-mer's heart. I just called
C A♭ B♭
heart, of my heart, of my
C
heart.

IF PARADISE IS HALF AS NICE

♩	113	8 Beat

```
        C           Em          C7   F   Fm   C   G4
Intro   La la la la, la la la la, ...

         C          Em               C7                 F
Ref.    If paradise is half as nice as heaven that you take me to,
         Fm              C                    G4
        who needs paradise? I'd rather have you!

                         C                Em                   C7                    F
Vers    They say paradise is up in the stars, but I needn't sigh because it's so far,
                           Fm                    C                         G4
        'cos I know it's worth a heaven on earth for me where you are.
                             C                       Em                  C7                   F
        A look from your eyes, a touch of your hand and I seem to fly to some other land
                           Fm                          C                        G4
        When you are around my heart always pounds just like a brass band.
```

Ref. ***Intro*** ***Ref.*** ***Intro*** ***Vers*** ***Intro*** *(fade out)*

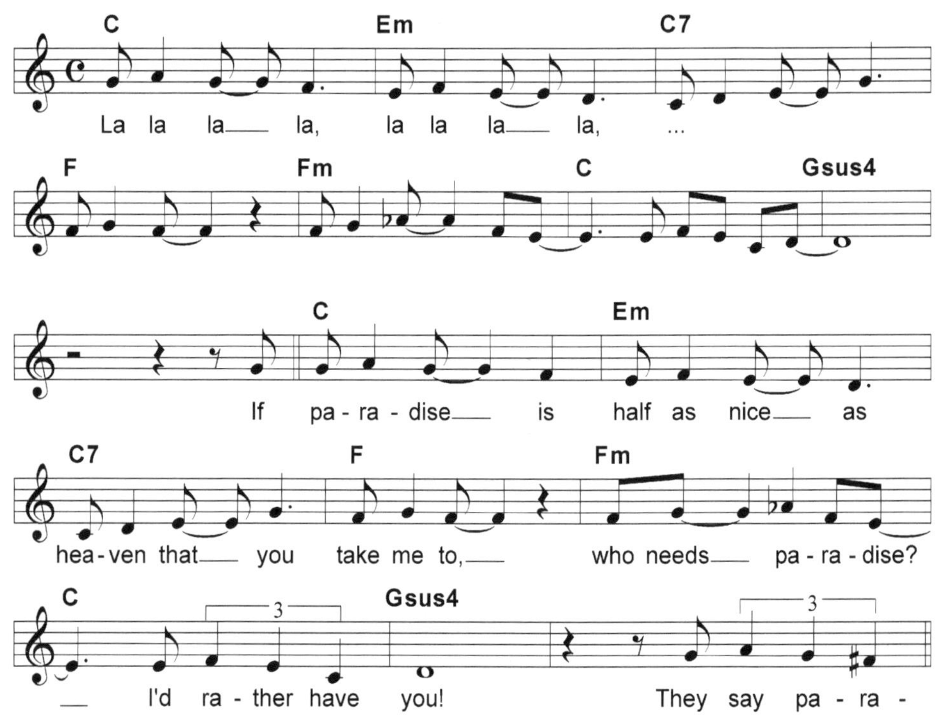

C
Em
dise is up in the stars, but I need-n't sigh
C7
F
be-cause it's so far, 'cos I know it's worth
Fm
C
3
Gsus4
a hea-ven on earth for me where you are.
3
C
A look from your eyes, a touch of your hand
Em
C7
and I seem to fly to some o-ther land.
F
Fm
When you are a-round my heart al-ways pounds
C
3
Gsus4
C
just like a brass band. If pa-ra-dise is
Em
C7
F
half as nice as hea-ven that you take me to,
Fm
C
3
Gsus4
D.C.
who needs pa-ra-dise? I'd ra-ther have you!

IF TOMORROW NEVER COMES

♩	79	Country-Ballad

```
                              Am7  D                                     C  G    G4  G
1.      Sometimes late at night,    I lie awake and watch her sleeping.
              D                 Am7
        She's lost in peaceful dreams,
                D                  C                 G    C  G
        so I turn off the lights and lay there in the dark.
                                       Am7
        And the thought crosses my mind,
        D                              C  G    G4  G
           if I never wake up in the morning,
          D            Am7       D          C                G    C  G
        would she ever doubt the way I feel about her in my heart.

                             C      G  C
Ref.    If tomorrow never comes,
                                     G          D  G
        will she know how much I loved her?
                             D      Am7            D
        Did I try in every way to show her every day
              C           G
        that she's my only one?
                                         C      G  C
        And if my time on earth were through,
                                   D       Em
        and she must face this world without me,
                                       Am7
        is the love I gave her in the past
               C            D                   G       D C G
        gonna be enough to last if tomorrow never comes?

                                       Am7  D                                 C      G
2.'     Cause I've lost loved ones in my life      who never knew how much I loved them.
        G4  G           D                Am7
                Now I live with the regret
                     D                  C             G     C  G
        that my true feelings for them never were revealed.
                                      Am7
        So I made a promise to myself,
        D                                C           G   G4  G
          to say each day how much she means to me,
             D                  Am7
        and avoid that circumstance
                              D                 C             G   C  G
        where there's no second chance to tell her how I feel.           Ref. ...

        (G)                                Am7        C                    D
             So, tell that someone that you love just what you're thinking of
                              G       D C G
        if tomorrow never comes.
```

Am7 D
1.Some - times late at night, I lie a - wake and watch her
C G Gsus4 G D Am7
sleep - ing. She's lost in peace - ful dreams, so I turn
D C G C
off the lights and lay there in the dark.
G Am7
And the thought cross - es my mind,
D C G Gsus4 G
if I nev - er wake up in the morn - ing,
D Am7 D C
would she ev - er doubt the way I feel a - bout her in my
G C G C G
heart. If to-mor - row nev - er comes,
C G D
will she know how much I loved her?
G D Am7
Did I try in eve - ry way to show her eve - ry day

D C G
_ that she's my on - ly one?
C G
And if my time on earth were through,
C D Em
and she must face this world with - out me,
Am7 C
is the love I gave her in the past gon - na be e - nough to
D G D C
last if to - mor - row nev - er comes?
G
2.'Cause I've lost loved ones in my
D.S.al
G Am7 C
So, tell that some - one that you love just what you're think - ing of
D G D C G
_ if to - mor - row nev - er comes.
rit.

IN THE ARMY NOW

♩	104	8 Rock-Ballad

```
Intro   Dm          Am7   Dm   C

        Dm
1.          A vacation in a foreign land, Uncle Sam does the best he can,
                          Gm          Am                         Dm
        you're in the army now, oh, oh, you're in the army now.

        Now you remember what the draftsman said, nothing to do all day but stay in bed,
                          Gm          Am                         Dm
        you're in the army now, oh, oh, you're in the army now.

        Dm
2.          You'll be a hero of the neighbourhood, nobody knows, that you left for good,
                          Gm          Am                         Dm
        you're in the army now, oh, oh, you're in the army now.

        Smiling faces as you wait to land, but once you get there no one gives a damn,
                          Gm          Am                         Dm
        you're in the army now, oh, oh, you're in the army now.

        Dm   Am7   Dm   C   Dm
Zw.                              Hand grenades flying over your head.

        Dm
3.          Missiles flying over your head, if you want to survive get out of bed,
                          Gm          Am                         Dm
        you're in the army now, oh, oh, you're in the army now.

        Shots ring out in the dead of night, the sergeant calls, "Stand up and fight!"
                          Gm          Am                         Dm
        You're in the army now, oh, oh, you're in the army now.

        Dm
4.         You've got your orders, better shoot on sight,

        your finger's on the trigger, but it doesn't seem right,
                              Gm          Am                         Dm
        //: you're in the army now, oh, oh, you're in the army now. ://

Zw.     Dm   Am7   Dm   C

        Dm
5.          Night is falling and you just can't see, is this illusion or reality,
                          Gm          Am                         Dm
        you're in the army now, oh, oh, you're in the army, in the army now.
                          Gm          Am                         Dm
        You're in the army now, oh, oh, you're in the army now.

            Gm    Am                            Dm
        //:         Oh, oh, you're in the army, in the army now. :// (fade out)
```

Words & Music by R. Bolland/ F. Bolland

Dm
Am7
Dm
C
Dm
1.A va-ca-tion in a
for-eign land,
Un-cle Sam does the
Gm
Am
best he can, you're in the ar-my now,
oh, oh, you're in the
Dm
ar-my now.
Now you re-mem-ber what the
drafts-man said,
noth-ing to do all day but
Gm
Am
stay in bed, you're in the ar-my now,
oh, oh, you're in the
Dm
Dm
Am7
ar-my now.

Dm
C
Dm
Hand gre-nades fly-ing o-ver your head.
D.S.al Coda
Drumms !
Am
Dm
oh, oh, you're in the ar-my, in the
Gm
Am
ar-my now. You're in the ar-my now, oh, oh, you're in the
Dm
Gm
ar-my now.
Am
Dm
Oh, oh, you're in the ar-my, in the ar-my now.
Wdhl. ad lib., dann fade out

I'M ON FIRE

♩ 176 Bossa-Beat

1. D: Hey little girl is your daddy home,
did he go away and leave you all alone? G: Mmh! Mmh!
I got a bad Bm: desire. G: Oh, oh, A: oh, I'm on D: fire.

2. D: Tell me now, baby, is he good to you,
can he do to you the things that I do? Oh G: now,
I can take you Bm: higher. G: Oh, oh, A: oh, I'm on D: fire.

Zw. Bm D Bm D

Sometimes it's like G: someone took a knife, baby,
edgy and dull and cut a D: six-inch valley through the middle of my Bm: soul.
At D: night I wake up with the sheets soaking wet
and a freight train running through the middle of my head.
Only G: you can cool my Bm: desire. G: Oh, oh, A: oh, I'm on D: fire.
G: Oh, oh, A: oh, I'm on D: fire. G: Oh, oh, A: oh, I'm on D: fire.

Outro //: Bm D :// Wdhl. nach Belieben, dann fade out

Words & Music by Bruce Springsteen

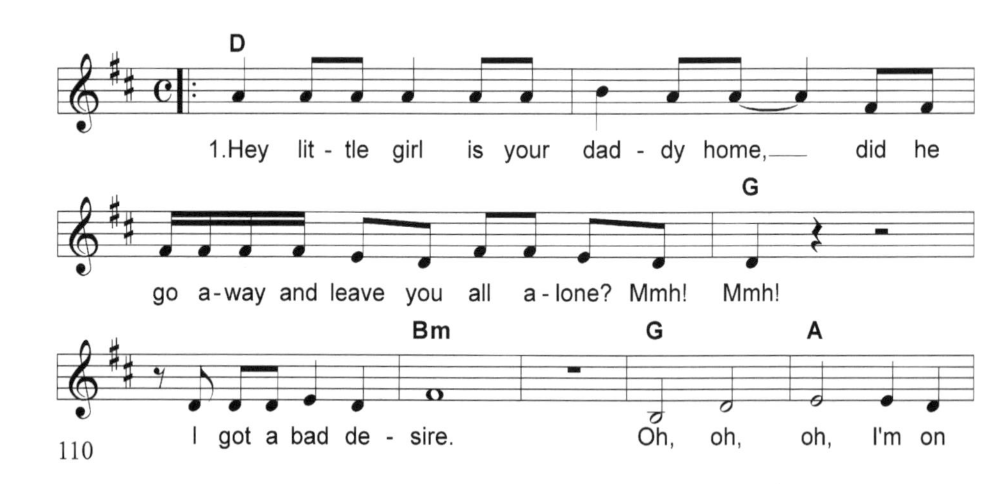

D
Bm
fire.
D
Bm
D
Some- times it's like
G
some - one took a knife, ba - by, ed - gy and dull and cut a
D
Bm
six-inch val - ley through the mid - dle of my soul.
D
At night I wake up with the sheets soak - ing wet and a
freight train run - ning through the mid - dle of my head. On - ly
G
Bm
you can cool my de - sire.
G
A
D
2 x
Bm
Oh, oh, oh, I'm on fire.
D
Wdhl. nach Belieben, dann fade out

IN THE SHADOWS

♩	106	Rock Beat

1.
Bm F#m Bm F#m
No sleep, no sleep until I'm done with finding the answer.
Bm F#m Bm F#m
Won't stop, won't stop before I find the cure for this cancer.
D F#m Bm F#m
Sometimes ---- I feel like going down, I'm so disconnected.
D F#m Bm F#m
Somehow ---- I know that I am haunted to be wanted.

Ref.
D F#m Bm F#m
I've been watching, I've been waiting in the shadows for my time.
D F#m Bm F#m
I've been searching, I've been living for tomorrows all my life.

Zw.
D F#m Bm F#m
Oh-oh! Oh-oh! Oh-oh! Oh-oh! In the shadows.
D F#m Bm F#m
Oh-oh! Oh-oh! Oh-oh! Oh-oh! In the shadows.

2.
Bm F#m Bm F#m
They say that I must learn to kill before I can feel safe.
Bm F#m Bm F#m
But I, I'd rather kill myself than turn into their slave.
D F#m Bm F#m
Sometimes ----- I feel that I should go and play with the thunder.
D F#m Bm F#m
Somehow ---- I just don't wanna stay and wait for a wonder.

Ref. I've been watching, ...

Zw.
D E F#m
Lately, I've been walking, walking in circles,

watching, waiting for something.
Bm F#m
Feel me, touch me, heal me, come take me higher.

Ref. I've been watching, ...

Zw.
D F#m
I've been watching!
Bm F#m
I've been waiting!
D F#m
I've been searching!
Bm F#m
I've been living for tomorrows!

Zw. Oh-oh! Oh-oh! In the shadows. ...

Ref. I've been watching, ... *(fade out)*

Bm
3
F♯m
1.No sleep, no sleep un - til I'm
Bm
F♯m
Bm
3
done with find - ing the ans - wer. Won't stop,
F♯m
Bm
won't stop be - fore I find the cure for this can -
F♯m
D
F♯m
- cer. Some - times I feel like go - ing
Bm
F♯m
down, I'm so dis - con - nec - ted.
D
F♯m
Some - how I know that I am
Bm
F♯m
haunt - ed to be want - ed. I've been watch -
D
F♯m
ing, I've been wait - ing in the sha -
Bm
F♯m
dows for my time. I've been search -

D F♯m Bm
ing, I've been liv - ing for to-mor - rows all my
F♯m D F♯m
life. Oh-oh! Oh - oh! Oh-oh! Oh - oh! In the sha-
Bm F♯m D
dows. Oh-oh! Oh - oh! Oh-oh! Oh -
F♯m Bm F♯m D.S.al Coda
oh! In the sha - dows. 2.They
F♯m D
life. Late - ly, I've been
E F♯m
walk - ing, walk - ing in circ - les, watch - ing,
Bm
wait - ing for some-thing. Feel me, touch me,
F♯m
heal me, come take me high-er.
D
I've been watch - ing, I've been wait -

F♯m Bm
ing in the sha - dows for my time.
F♯m D
I've been search - ing, I've been liv -
F♯m Bm F♯m
ing for to-mor-rows all my life. I've been watch-
D F♯m Bm F♯m
ing! I've been wait-ing! I've been search-
D F♯m Bm
ing! I've been liv - ing for to-mor -
F♯m D F♯m
rows! Oh-oh! Oh - oh! Oh-oh! Oh - oh! In the sha-
Bm F♯m D
dows. Oh-oh! Oh - oh! Oh-oh! Oh -
F♯m Bm F♯m
oh! In the sha - dows. I've been watch -
D.S.and fade out

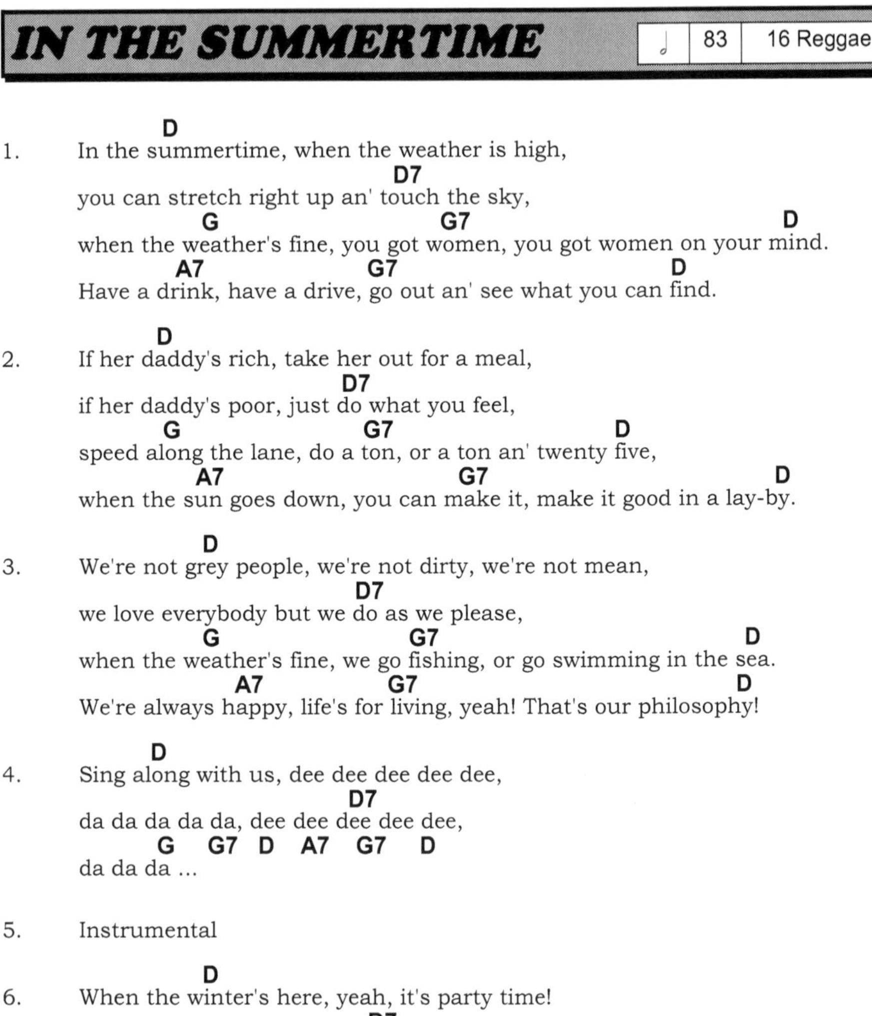

IN THE SUMMERTIME

𝅗𝅥	83	16 Reggae

1.
D
In the summertime, when the weather is high,
D7
you can stretch right up an' touch the sky,
G G7 D
when the weather's fine, you got women, you got women on your mind.
A7 G7 D
Have a drink, have a drive, go out an' see what you can find.

2.
D
If her daddy's rich, take her out for a meal,
D7
if her daddy's poor, just do what you feel,
G G7 D
speed along the lane, do a ton, or a ton an' twenty five,
A7 G7 D
when the sun goes down, you can make it, make it good in a lay-by.

3.
D
We're not grey people, we're not dirty, we're not mean,
D7
we love everybody but we do as we please,
G G7 D
when the weather's fine, we go fishing, or go swimming in the sea.
A7 G7 D
We're always happy, life's for living, yeah! That's our philosophy!

4.
D
Sing along with us, dee dee dee dee dee,
D7
da da da da da, dee dee dee dee dee,
G G7 D A7 G7 D
da da da ...

5. Instrumental

6.
D
When the winter's here, yeah, it's party time!
D7
Bring a bottle, wear your bright clothes, it'll soon be summertime,
G G7 D
and we'll sing again, we'll go driving, or maybe we'll settle down,
A7 G7 D
if she's rich, if she's nice, bring your friends, an' we'll all go into town.

Wiederhole: 1.-2.-3.-4. – dann fade out

Words & Music by Ray Dorset

D
1.In the summer-time, when the weath-er is high, you can
D7
stretch right up an' touch the sky, when the
G
G7
weath-er's fine, you got wo-men, you got wo-men on your
D
A7
mind. Have a drink, have a drive,
G7
1.-5.
D
go out an' see what you can find.
6.
D
2.If her (6.)town.

IRONIC

♩ 85 | 16 Beat

```
        G      C  G                   Am
1.      An old man turned ninety-eight.
                      G    C      G              Am
        He won the lottery and died the next day.
                  G   C          G          Am
        It's a black fly in your chardonnay.
                 G        C         G          Am
        It's a death row pardon two minutes too late
                      G     C           G     Am
        and isn't it ironic,    don't you think?

                   G   C             G         Am
Ref.    It's like rain---- on your wedding day.
                     G   C               G        Am
        It's a free ride---- when you've already paid.
                         G   C             G         Am
        It's the good advice---- that you just didn't take
                  Bb             F         G
        and who would've thought, it figures.

                   G      C         G       Am
2.      Mister Play it safe was afraid to fly.
                         G  C                  G         Am
        He packed his suitcase and kissed his kids good-bye.
                          G          C    G          Am
        He waited his whole damn life to take that flight
                      G                C                      G          Am
        and as the plane crashed down he thought: "Well, isn't this nice?"
                      G     C           G     Am
        and isn't it ironic,    don't you think?

Ref.    It's like rain ...

            Fj7                                     Cj7/G
Zw.     Well life has a funny way of sneaking up on you,
                                                   Fj7                               Cj7/G
        when you think everything's okay and everything's going right.--------
            Fj7                                    Cj7/G
        And life has a funny way of helping you out

        when you think everything's gone wrong
            Fj7                                 Cj7/G
        and everything blows up in your face.--------

             G   C         G                Am
3.      A traffic jam when you're already late,
                  G       C          G          Am
        a no-smoking sign on your cigarette break.
                   G                C                    G         Am
        It's like ten thousand spoons when all you need is a knife.
               G                        C                 G                   Am
        It's meeting the man of my dreams and then meeting his beautiful wife.
```

G C G Am
And isn't it ironic, don't you think?
G C G Am
A little too ironic, and yeah, I really do think.

G C Bb F G Fj7 Cj7/G
Ref. It's like rain ... ... and who would've thought, it figures.

Fj7 Cj7/G
And life has a funny way of sneaking up on you.
Fj7 Cj7/G Fj7
Life has a funny, funny way of helping you out, helping you out.

Words by Alanis Morissette Music by Alanis Morissette & Glen Ballard

G C G Am
on your wed-ding day. It's a free ride
G C G Am
when you've al-rea-dy paid. It's the good ad-vice
G C G Am
that you just did-n't take and
B♭ F 1. G 2. G
who would-'ve thought, it fi-gures. 2.Mis-ter gures. Well
FMaj7
life has a fun-ny way of sneak-ing up on
CMaj7/G
you, when you think eve-ry-thing's o-kay and
FMaj7 CMaj7/G
eve-ry-thing's going right. And

FMaj7
life has a fun - ny way of help - ing you out
CMaj7/G
when you think eve - ry - thing's gone wrong and
FMaj7
CMaj7
eve - ry - thing blows up in your face.
3.A
D.S.al
G
FMaj7
CMaj7/G
gures.
And
FMaj7
CMaj7/G
life has a fun - ny way of sneak - ing up on you.
FMaj7
CMaj7/G
Life has a fun - ny, fun - ny way of help - ing you out,
FMaj7
help - ing you out.

JUST LIKE A PILL

♩	102	Rock

1.
G Em C D
I'm lying here on the floor, where you left me, I think I took to much.
G Em C D
I'm crying here, what have you done? I thought it would be fun.

Br.
C D C
I can't stay on your life support there's a shortage in a switch,
D C
I can't stay on your morphine, cause it's making me itch,
D C
I said I tried to call the nurse again, but she's being a little bitch,
D
I think I'll get out of here.

Ref.
G Em C
Where I can run, just as fast as I can, to the middle of nowhere,
D
to the middle of my frustrated fears,
G Em C
and I swear you're just like a pill, instead of making me better,
D G (Em C D)
you keep making me ill, you keep making me ill.

2.
G Em C D
I haven't moved from the spot where you left me, it must be a bad trip.
G Em C D
All of the other pills, they were different, maybe I should get some help.

Br. I can't stay ...

Ref. Where I can run,... *(2x)*

Br. I can't stay ...

Ref. Where I can run,... *(4x, fade out)*

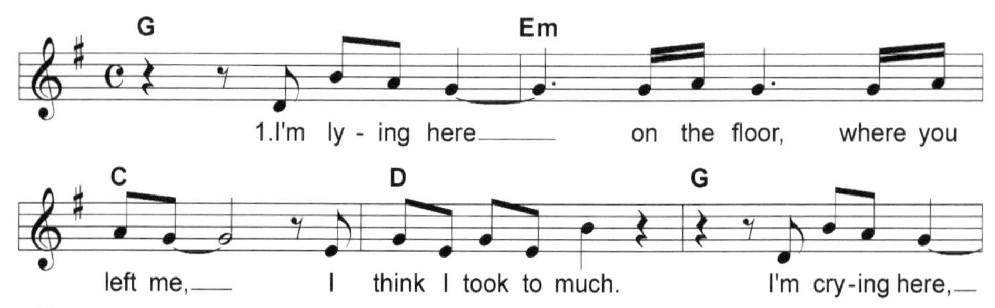

Words & Music by Alecia Moore & Dallas Austin

KILLING ME SOFTLY

𝅗𝅥	60	16 Ballad

(Frei im Tempo)

Em **Am** **D7** **G**
Ref.: Strumming my pain with his fingers, singing my life with his words.
Em **A** **D** **C**
Killing me softly with his song, killing me softly with his song.
G **C** **F** **E**
Telling my whole life with his words, killing me softly with his song.

(im Tempo)
Instr.: **//: D7/4 D7 D7/4 D7 ://**

Am7 **D7** **G** **C**
1. I heard he sang a good song, I heard he had a style,
Am7 **D7** **Em**
and so I came to see him and listen for a while.
Am7 **D7** **G** **B7**
And there he was this young boy, a stranger to my eyes. Ref.: ...

Am7 **D7** **G** **C**
2. I felt all flushed with fever, embarrassed by the crowd,
Am7 **D7** **Em**
I felt he found my letters and read each one out loud.
Am7 **D7** **G** **B7**
I prayed that he would finish, but he just kept right on. Ref.: ...

Am7 **D7** **G** **C**
3. He sang as if he knew me, in all my dark despair.
Am7 **D7** **Em**
And then he looked right through me, as if I wasn't there.
Am7 **D7** **G** **B7**
And he just kept on singing, singing clear and strong. Ref.: ...

Em **Am7** **D** **G**
Outro: He was strumming my pain, yeah, he was singing my life.
Em **A** **D** **C**
Killing me softly with his song, killing me softly with his song.
G **C** **F** **E**
Telling my whole life with his words, killing me softly with his song.

Words & Music by Charles Fox, Norman Gimbel

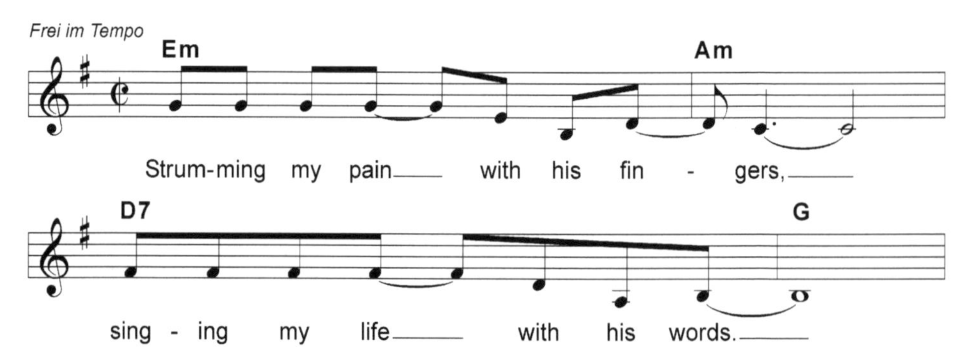

Em
A
Kil - ling me soft - ly with his song, kill - ing me soft -
D
C
G
- ly with his song. Tell-ing my whole life with his
C
F
D
words, kill-ing me soft - ly with his his song.
D7sus4
D7
D7sus4
D7
im Tempo
Am7
D7
I heard he sang a good song,
G
C
Am7
I heard he had a style, and so I came
D7
Em
to see him and list - en for a while.
Am7
D7
G
And there he was this young boy, a stran-ger

B7 Em Am
to my eyes. Strum - ming my pain with his fin - gers,
D7 G Em
sing - ing my life with his words. Kil - ling me soft - ly with his
A D
song, kill - ing me soft - ly with his
C G C
song. Tell - ing my whole life with his words, kill - kill - ing me
1. F E 2. F
soft - ly with his song. soft - ly
E Em
with his song. He was strum - ming my pain,
Am7 D G
yeah, he was sing - ing my life.
Em D.S.al Coda F E
Kill - ing me soft - ly with his soft - ly with his song.

LIEBE IST ALLES

♩	91	8 Ballad

```
        Am
1.      Hast du nur ein Wort zu sagen,
        F                   G
          nur ein' Gedanken, dann lass es Liebe sein.
         Am
        Kannst du mir ein Bild beschreiben
        F                   G
          mit deinen Farben, dann lass es Liebe sein.
         Em      C      Em    C
        Wann Du gehst, wieder gehst.

                   F             G              Em          Am
Ref.    Schau mir noch mal ins Gesicht, sag's mir oder sag es nicht.
                  F            G              Em              Am
        Dreh dich bitte noch mal um und ich seh's in deinem Blick.
                F     G   Em  Am            F    G   Em  Am
        Lass es Liebe sein.          Lass es Liebe sein.

         Am
2.      Hast du nur noch einen Tag,
        F                  G
          nur eine Nacht, dann lass es Liebe sein.
         Am
        Hast du nur noch eine Frage,
        F                           G
          die ich nie zu fragen wage, dann lass es Liebe sein.
         Em      C      Em    C
        Wann Du gehst, wieder gehst.      Ref. ...

              F              G                 Em            Am
        Das ist alles, was wir brauchen, noch viel mehr als große Worte.
                F          G           Em         Am
        Lass das alles hinter dir, fang noch mal von vorne an.
        F           G     Em         Am
          Denn Liebe ist alles,       Liebe ist alles,
        F          G     Em           Am
          Liebe ist alles, alles was wir brauchen.
        F          G     Em        Am
          Liebe ist alles,      Liebe ist alles,
        F          G     Em           Am
          Liebe ist alles, alles was wir brauchen.
                F          G Em Am F G Em Am
        Lass es Liebe sein. --------------
              F              G                 Em            Am
        Das ist alles, was wir brauchen, noch viel mehr als große Worte.
                F          G           Em         Am
        Lass das alles hinter dir, fang noch mal von vorne an.
        F          G     Em        Am
          Liebe ist alles,      Liebe ist alles,
        F          G     Em           Am
          Liebe ist alles, alles was wir brauchen.
                F          G Em  Am          F G           Em  Am
        Lass es Liebe sein. -------------- Lass es Lie----be sein. ----------

        F G Em Am F G Em Am F G Em Am
```

Music by Peter Plate, Ulf Leo Sommer   Words by Peter Plate, Ulf Leo Sommer, Ana Neuenhofen

Am F
1.Hast du nur ein Wort zu sa-gen, nur ein' Ge-dan-ken,
G
dann lass es Lie - be sein.
Am F
Kannst du mir ein Bild be-schrei-ben mit dei-nen Far-ben,
G Em
dann lass es Lie-be sein. Wann Du gehst,
C Em C
wie - der gehst. Schau mir
F G Em Am
noch mal ins Ge-sicht, sag's mir o - der sag es nicht. Dreh dich
F G Em Am
bit - te noch mal um und ich seh's in dei - nem Blick. Lass es
F G Em Am F G 1. Em Am
Lie-be sein. Lass es Lie - be sein.
2. Em Am F G
Das ist al - les, was wir brau - chen, noch viel

Em Am F G
mehr als gro - ße Wor - te. Lass das al - les hin - ter dir, fang noch
Em Am F G Em Am
mal von vor - ne an. Denn Lie - be ist al - les, Lie - be ist al - les,
F G Em Am
Lie - be ist al - les, al - les was wir brau - chen.
F G Em Am F G
Lie - be ist al - les, Lie - be ist al - les, Lie - be ist al - les,
Em Am F G Em Am
al - les was wir brau - chen. Lass es Lie - be sein.
F G Em Am F G
D.S.al
Das ist Lie - be ist al - les,
Em Am F G
Lie - be ist al - les, Lie - be ist al - les,
Em Am F G Em Am
al - les was wir brau - chen. Lass es Lie - be sein. Lass es
F G Em Am F G Em Am
Lie - be sein.
2x wdhl.

LAY BACK IN THE ARMS OF SOMEONE

♩	123	8 Pop-Beat

1.
G If you want my **D** sympathy **G** just open your **D** heart to me,
G you'll get whatever **D** you'll ever **A** need.
G You think that's too **D** high for you, but **G** baby, I would **D** die for you,
G when there's nothing **D** left, you know where I'll **A** be.

Ref.
D You lay back in the **Bm** arms of someone, **D** you give in to the **Em** charms of someone
G you lay back in the **A** arms of someone **D** you **A** love.
D Lay back in the **Bm** arms of someone. **D** When you feel you're a **Em** part of someone,
G lay back in the **A** arms of someone **D** you love.

Zw. **G D G D G D A**

2.
G So baby, just **D** call on me **G** when you want **D** all of me,
G I'll be your **D** lover, I'll be **A** your friend.
G There's nothing that **D** I won't do, 'cause **G** baby, I just **D** live for you
G with nothing to **D** hide, no need to **A** pretend. ***Ref. ...*** ***Zw. ...***

Oh I **G** know you think that's too **D** high for you, oh but **G** baby,
I would **D** die for you. **G** When there's nothing **D** left I'll be with **A** you. ***Ref. ...***

Zw. *(fade out)*

Words & Music by Nicky Chinn, Mike Chapman

G D G
ba-by, I would die for you, when there's noth-ing
D A D
left, you know where I'll be. You lay back in the
Bm D Em
arms of some - one, you give in to the charms of some - one,
G A D
you lay back in the arms of some-one you love.
A D Bm
Lay back in the arms of some - one.
D Em
When you feel you're a part of some - one,
G A D
lay back in the arms of some-one you love.
G D G
D G D
1.
A
D.S.and fade out (im Zwischenspiel)
2.
A G
Oh I know you think that's too

LIGHT MY FIRE

♩	128	8 Beat

Intro **G D F B♭ E♭ A♭ A**

```
          Am7                            F#m7      Am7                         F#m7
1.   You know that it would be untrue, you know that I would be a liar.
     Am7                  F#m7   Am7                       F#m7
     If I was to say to you    Girl, we couldn't get much higher.

      G        A           D
Ref. Come on baby, light my fire!
      G        A           D    B
     Come on baby, light my fire!
      G              D      E    (E7)
     Try to set the night on fire!

        Am7                          F#m7      Am7                         F#m7
2.   The time to hesitate is through, no time to wallow in the mire.
      Am7                       F#m7           Am7                     F#m7
     Try now we can only lose and our love become a funeral pyre.

          F              C       D    F              C        D
Zw.  //: Try to set the night on fire! Try to set the night on fire! ://
```

Outro **G D F B♭ E♭ A♭ A**

Words & Music by Jim Morrison, Robbie Krieger, Ray Manzarek & John Densmore

Am7 F♯m7 Am7
know that I would be a liar.
If I was to say to you
F♯m7 Am7 F♯m7
Girl, we could-n't get much high - er.
G A D
Come on ba - by, light my fi - re!
G A D B G D
Come on ba-by, light my fi - re!
Try to set the night on
E E7 D.S.al Coda
fi-re!
2.The
F C
Try to set the night on fi -
D F C D
- re!
Try to set the night on fi - re!
G D F B♭
E♭ A♭ A

LIKE A PRAYER

♩ 112 | Pop-Reggae

```
              Dm                C/D   C7/D Dm                        C/D C7/D  Dm
Intro              Life is a mys—te----ry,   everyone must stand a------lone.
                              C/E  C7/B♭    F/A  B♭     F/C  C     Dm
              I hear you call my         name and it feels like home.

              F                         C                            B♭
Ref.1            When you call my name it's like a little prayer.
                                      F/A            Dm        F
              I'm down on my knees, I wanna take you there.
                                    C                               B♭                   F/A
              In the midnight hour I can feel your power just like a prayer.
                            Dm            (B♭)
              You know I'll take you (there.)

                                F     C                  Dm
1.            I hear your voice,        it's like an angel sighing.
              B♭                F                       C
                  I have no choice, I hear your voice, feels like flying.
              B♭                  F     C                 Dm
                  I close my eyes,       oh God, I think I'm falling
              B♭                    F                C
                  out of the sky, I close my eyes, heaven help me.                Ref.1 ...

                           F   C                      Dm
2.            Like a child        you whisper softly to me.
              B♭                     F                        C
                  You're in control just like a child. Now I'm dancing.
              B♭                    F     C                 Dm
                  It's like a dream,       no end and no beginning.
              B♭                         F                   C
                  You're here with me, it's like a dream, let the choir sing.     Ref.1 ...

                 F                              C                           B♭
Ref.2         (there.) When you call my name it's like a little prayer.
                                      F/A            Dm        F
              I'm down on my knees, I wanna take you there.
                                    C                               B♭                   F/A
              In the midnight hour I can feel your power just like a prayer.
                            Dm                   C/D    Dm    C/D
              You know I'll take you there.

              Dm                C/D  Dm                       C/D     Dm
Zw.                Life is a mystery, everyone must stand alone.
                              C/E    B♭ F/A   B♭        F/C C     Dm
              I hear you call my name and it feels like home.
                                     C/D
              Just like a prayer,         your voice can take me there.
              Dm                                 C/D
                  Just like a muse to me,          you are a mystery.
              Dm                            C/E                    B♭
                  Just like a dream,           you are not what you seem.
              F/A        B♭                   C4                           C           F
                  Just like a prayer, no choice your voice can take me there.
```

(F) C
//: Just like a prayer, I'll take you there.
B♭ Am Dm
It's like a dream to me. :// *(3x wdhl.)*

Dm C/D
//: Just like a prayer, your voice can take me there.
Dm C/D
Just like a muse to me, you are a mystery.
Dm C/E B♭
Just like a dream, you are not what you seem.
F/A B♭ C4 C Dm
Just like a prayer, no choice your voice can take me there. :// *(fade out)*

F/A Dm Bb F
er. You know I'll take you there. 1.I hear your voice,
C Dm Bb
it's like an an - gel sigh-ing. I have no choice,
F C Bb
I hear your voice, feels like fly-ing. I close my eyes,
F C Dm Bb
oh God, I think I'm fall-ing out of the
F C
sky, I close my eyes, hea-ven help me.
2x D.S.
(2.mal al Coda
F C
there. When you call my name it's like a lit-tle pray-
Bb F/A Dm
er. I'm down on my knees, I wan-na take you
F C Bb
there. In the mid-night hour I can feel your po-wer just like a pray-
F/A Dm C/D Dm C/D
er. You know I'll take you there.

Dm C/D Dm C/D
Life is a mys - te - ry, eve - ry - one must stand a - lone.
Dm C/E B♭ F/A B♭ F/C C
I hear you call my name and it feels like
Dm C/D
(home.) Just like a pray - er, your voice can take me there.
Dm C/D
Just like a muse to me, you are a mys - te - ry.
Dm C/E B♭
3
Just like a dream, you are not what you seem.
F/A B♭ Csus4 C
Just like a pray - er, no choice your voice can take me
F C
(there.) Just like a pray - er, I'll take you there.
B♭ Am Dm
(3x wdhl.)
It's like a dream to me.
D.S.(fade out)

LONELY PEOPLE

♩ 156 Country Fox

1.
G Em Bm G Em Bm D
This is for all the lonely people thinking that life has passed them by.
C D G G/F# Em G/D
Don't give up until you drink from the silver cup
C D G D
and ride that highway in the sky.

2.
G Em Bm G Em Bm D
This is for all the single people thinking that love has left them dry.
C D G G/F# Em G/D
Don't give up until you drink from the silver cup
C D G
you never know until you try.

Zw.
C Bm Am C Bm Am C Bm Am D7 G
Well, I'm on my way, yes, I'm back to stay, well, I'm on my way back home.

Solo G D4 F D7 G D4 F D7 G D7 Em Bm Em Bm Em Bm D D7

3.
G Em Bm G Em Bm D
This is for all the lonely people thinking that life has passed them by.
C D G G/F# Em G/D
Don't give up until you drink from the silver cup
C D
and never take you down or
G G/F# Em G/D C D Em
never give you up, you never know until you try.

Musik und Text: Daniel Milton Peek

D
1. G D
2. G
high-way in the sky.
try.
Well, I'm
C Bm Am
C Bm Am
on my way,
yes, I'm back to stay,
C Bm Am D7 G
well, I'm on my way back home.
G Dsus4 F D7
1. G
2. G D7
Em Bm Em Bm
Em Bm D D7
D.C.al
C D
and ne - ver take you down or
G G/F♯ Em G/D
ne - ver give you up,
C D Em
you ne - ver know un - til you try.

LOVE HURTS

♩	80	Rock-Ballad

```
           G          Em         C           D
1.    Love hurts, love scars, love wounds and mars
      C     G       Em         C      D
      any heart not tough or strong enough
         D7            G    B7          Em
      to take a lot of pain, take a lot of pain.
      B7             C                  D
      Love is like a cloud, holds a lot of rain.
        C    G    F   C         G
      Love hurts, ooh, ooh, love hurts.

          G         Em     C     D
2.    I'm young I know but even so
      C          G       Em      C            D
      I know a thing or two I've learned from you
            D7            G    B7            Em
      I've really learned a lot, really learned a lot.
      B7            C                          D
      Love is like a flame, it burns you when it's hot.
        C    G    F   C          G
      Love hurts, ooh, ooh, love hurts.

         Em                 B7    Em    B7      Em     B7    Em
Zw.   Some folks think of happiness, blissfulness, togetherness.
        A7                                                  D
      Some folks fool themselves I guess, they're not fooling me.
          C           G      B7          Em
      I know it isn't true, I know it isn't true.
      B7            C                     D
      Love is just a lie made to make you blue.
        C    G    F   C         G     F    C        G
      Love hurts, ooh, ooh, love hurts, ooh, ooh, love hurts.

           D7         G      B7          Em
      I know it isn't true, I know it isn't true.
      B7            C                     D
      Love is just a lie made to make you blue.
        C   G     F   C          G    F    C        G     F    C
      Love hurts, ooh, ooh, love hurts, ooh, ooh, love hurts. Ooh, ooh!
```

Words & Music by Boudleaux Bryant

G
Em
C
D
C
1.Love hurts, love scars, love wounds and mars an - y
G
Em
C
D
D7
heart not tough or strong e - nough to take a lot of
G
B7
Em
B7
C
pain, take a lot of pain, Love is like a cloud, holds a lot of
D
C
G
F
C
G
1.
rain. Love hurts, ooh, ooh, love hurts.
2.I'm
2.
Em
B7
Em
B7
Em
Some folks think of hap - pi - ness, bliss - ful - ness, to -
B7
Em
A7
geth - er - ness. Some folks fool them - selves I guess,
D
C
G
B7
they're not fool - ing me I know it is - n't true, I know it is - n't
Em
B7
C
D
C
true. Love is just a lie made to make you blue. Love
G
F
C
G
F
C
hurts, ooh, ooh, love hurts, ooh, ooh, love
G
D7
D.S.al Coda
F
C
hurts. I know it is - n't
Ooh, ooh!
rit.

MANDY

𝅗𝅥	52	Ballad

```
        G                         D/G   G                           D/G
1.      I remember all my life, raining down as cold as ice.
          Am                         C/G
        Shadows of a man, a face through a window,
         F                             D4
        cryin' in the night, the night goes into

          G                              D/G  G                          D/G
2.      morning, just another day, happy people pass my way.
         Am                              C/G
        Looking in their eyes, I see a memory,
           F                         D4
        I never realized how happy you made me.

              G                    Em                C                 D
Ref.    Oh, Mandy, well, you came and you gave without taking.
               D4                       G
        But I sent you away. Oh, Mandy,
                   Em                C                   D
        well you kissed me and stopped me from shaking,
                D4                        G       (Em  C  D4       )
        and I need you today. Oh, Mandy!

              G                               D/G      G                              D/G
3.      I'm standing on the edge of time, I walked away when love was mine.
          Am                            C/G
        Caught up in a world of uphill climbing,
             F                                   D4
        the tears are in my mind, and nothin' is rhyming.               Ref. ...

Zw.     (Em)   Bm   C   Am   D4   D

         Am                          C/G
Br.     Yesterday's a dream, I face the morning,
          F                             D4
        crying on the breeze, the pain is calling.                      Ref. ...

              G                         C     G
Ref.    Oh, Mandy, ...    ... and I need you.

            G/F#                  Em                 C           D
        Oh, Mandy, won't you listen to what I got to say?
                                  D4
        Oh, Mandy, don't you leave me, going overway.
        G          G/F#                    Em                C           D
           Oh, Mandy, won't you listen to what I got to say?
              C/D                          G        D/G    C    Em  D/F#  G
        And I need you today, oh, Mandy.
```

G D/G
1.I re - mem - ber all my life,
G D/G Am
rain - ing down as cold as ice. Sha - dows of a man, a
C/G F
face through a win - dow, cry - in' in the night, the
Dsus4 G D/G
night goes in - to 2.mor - ning, just a - no - ther day,
G D/G Am
hap - py peo - ple pass my way. Look - ing in their eyes, I
C/G F
see a me - mo - ry, I ne - ver re - a - lized how
Dsus4 G
hap - py you made me. Oh, Man - dy, well, you came
Em C D
and you gave with - out ta - king. But I

Dsus4
G
sent you a - way. Oh, Man - dy, well you kissed
Em
C
D
me and stopped me from sha - king, and I
Dsus4
G
Em C Dsus4
need you to - day. Oh, Man-dy!
Em
Bm
C
3.I'm
D.S.al
Man - dy!
Am
Dsus4
D
Am
Yes - ter - day's a dream,
C/G
F
Dsus4
I face the morn - ing, cry - ing on the breeze, the pain is cal - ling. Oh,
G
Em
C
Man - dy, well, you came and you gave with - out ta -
D
Dsus4
- king. But I sent you a - way. Oh, Man -

G Em C
- dy, well you kissed me and stopped me from sha -
D 1. Dsus4 2. C
- king, and I need you to - day. Oh, need
G G/F♯ Em C
you. Oh, Man - dy, won't you lis - ten to what I got to say?
D Dsus4
Oh, Man - dy, don't you leave me, go - ing o - ver - way.
G G/F♯ Em C D
Oh, Man-dy, won't you lis-ten to what I got to say? And I
C/D G D/G C Em D/F♯ G
need you to-day, oh, Man-dy.
rit.

MAN ON THE MOON

♩	119	Rhumba Beat

```
     C                          D          C
1.   Mott the Hoople and the game of Life,    yeah, yeah, yeah, yeah.
                                D          C
     Andy Kaufman in the wrestling match,     yeah, yeah, yeah, yeah.
                                 D              C
     Monopoly, Twenty one, checkers, and chess,    yeah, yeah, yeah, yeah.
                                    D         C
     Mister Fred Blasy, and the breakfast mess,    yeah, yeah, yeah, yeah.
                            D        C
     Let's play Twister, let's play Risk,    yeah, yeah, yeah, yeah.
                                        D        C
     I'll see you in heaven if you make the list,    yeah, yeah, yeah, yeah.

         Am                               G     Am                              G
Ref.1. Now Andy did you hear about this one, tell me, are you locked in the punch?
     Am                       G          C    D
     Andy are you goofing on Elvis, hey baby,    are we losin' touch?
     G          Am   C          Bm              G     Am          D
     If you believed    they put a man on the moon, man on the moon.
     G         Am   C            Bm              Am
     If you believe    there's nothing up their sleeve and nothing is cruel.

     C                                   D          C
2.   Moses went walking with the staff of wood,    yeah, yeah, yeah, yeah.
                                  D          C
     Newton got beaned by the apple good,    yeah, yeah, yeah, yeah.
                                     D           C
     Egypt was troubled by the horrible asp,    yeah, yeah, yeah, yeah.
                                       D          C
     Mister Charles Darwin had the gall to ask,    yeah, yeah, yeah, yeah.

         Am                               G     Am                              G
Ref.2. Now Andy did you hear about this one, tell me, are you locked in the punch?
     Am                       G          C    D
     Andy are you goofing on Elvis, hey baby,    are you having fun? If you believed ..

Zw.  Em  D  Em  D  Em  D

     C                               D              C
3.   Here's a little agit for the never-believer,    yeah, yeah, yeah, yeah.
                                    D        C
     Here's a little ghost for the offering,    yeah, yeah, yeah, yeah.
                              D              C
     Here's a truck stop instead of Saint Peter's,    yeah, yeah, yeah, yeah.
                                      D       C
     Mister Andy Kaufman's gone wrestling,    yeah, yeah, yeah, yeah.  Ref.1. ...

Zw.  Em  D  Em  D  Em  D

        G            Am   C          Bm              G     Am          D
     //: If you believed    they put a man on the moon, man on the moon.
     G         Am   C            Bm              Am                          Em
     If you believe    there's nothing up their sleeve and nothing is cruel. ://
                                                                    (2x wdhl.)
```

1.Mott the Hoo - ple and the game of Life,
yeah, yeah, yeah, yeah.
An - dy Kauf - man in the
wrest-ling match,
yeah, yeah, yeah, yeah.
Mo-
no - po - ly, Twen - ty one, check - ers, and chess,
yeah, yeah, yeah, yeah.
Mis-ter Fred Bla-sy, and the
break-fast mess,
yeah, yeah, yeah, yeah.
Let's play Twis - ter, let's play Risk,
yeah, yeah, yeah, yeah.
I'll see you in hea - ven if you
make the list,
yeah, yeah, yeah, yeah.
Now
An-dy did you hear a-bout this one,
tell me, are you locked in the punch?

G Am G C
An-dy are you goof-ing on El - vis, hey ba-by,
D G Am
are we los-in' touch? If you be-lieved
C Bm G Am D
they put a man on the moon, man on the moon.
G Am C Bm
If you be-lieve there's noth-ing up their sleeve
Am Em D Em D
and noth-ing is cruel.
Em D
D.S.al Coda
D G Am
If you be-lieved
C Bm G Am
they put a man on the moon, man on the moon.
D G Am C Bm
If you be-lieve there's noth-ing up their sleeve
Am Em
and noth-ing is cruel.

ME AND BOBBY MCGEE

♩	93	Folk

```
            G
1.          Busted flat in Baton Rouge, headin' for a train,
                                         D7
            feelin' nearly faded as my jeans,
            Bobby thumbed a diesel down just before it rained.
                                            G
            Took us all the way to New Orleans.
            I took my harpoon out of my dirty, red bandanna
                                         G7                C
            and was blowin' sad while Bobby sang the blues
            with them windshield wipers slappin' time
                 G                              D                              D7
            and Bobby clappin' hands we fin'ly sang up ev'ry song that driver knew.

             C                                  G
Ref.        Freedom's just another word for nothin' left to lose,
             D7                                    G
            nothin' ain't worth nothin' but it's free.
            C                                      G
            Feelin' good was easy, Lord, when Bobby sang the blues.
                D
            And feelin' good was good enough for me,
             D7                                    G
            good enough for me and Bobby McGee.

                          G
2.          From the coalmines of Kentucky to the California sun,
                                               D7
            Bobby shared the secrets of my soul.
            Standing right beside me, Lord, through everything I done
                                                     G
            and every night he kept me from the cold.
            Then somewhere near Salina, Lord, I let him slip away,
                              G7                     C
            looking for the home and I hope he'll find.
                                                     G
            And I'll trade all my tomorrows for a single yesterday,
             D                                     D7
            holding Bobby's body next to mine.
```

Ref. Freedom's just another word ...

3. La, la, la, ...

Ref. Freedom's just another word ...

4. *Instrumental – fade out*

G
1.Bust - ed flat in Ba - ton Rouge, head - in' for a train,
D7
feel - in' near - ly fad - ed as my jeans,
Bob - by thumbed a die - sel down just be - fore it rained.
G
Took us all the way to New Or - leans. I
took my har - poon out of my dir - ty, red ban - dan - na and was
G7
C
blow - in' sad while Bob - by sang the blues with them
G
wind - shield wi - pers slapp - in' time and Bob - by clapp - in' hands we fin' - ly
D
D7
sang up ev' - ry song that dri - ver knew.

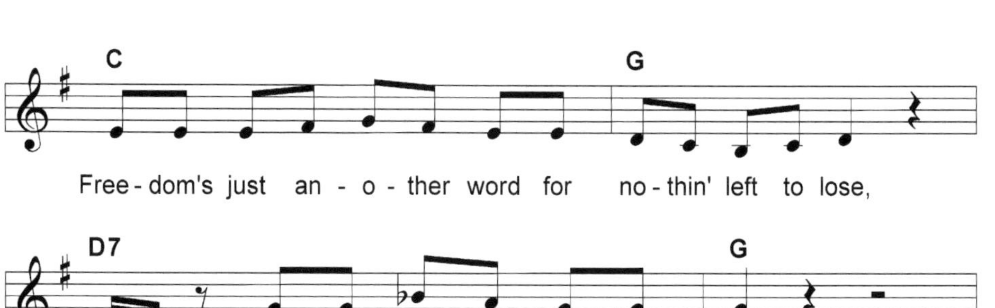
C
G
Free-dom's just an-o-ther word for no-thin' left to lose,

D7
G
no-thin' ain't worth no-thin' but it's free.

C
G
Feel-in' good was ea-sy, Lord, when Bob-by sang the blues. And

D
feel-in' good was good e-nough for me,

D7
G
D.C.
good e-nough for me and Bob-by Mc-Gee. 2.From the

MY HEART WILL GO ON

(Love Theme From 'Titanic')

♩	99	Ballad

```
        C                  G             F          C    G
1.      Every night in my dreams I see you, I feel you,
          C                G            F    G7
        that is how I know you go on.
          C                G                 F           C    G
        Far across the distance and spaces between us
          C                      G              F
        you have come to show you go on.

          Am   G          F           G          Am                G                  F    G7
Ref.1   Near, far, wherever you are, I believe that the heart does go on.
        Am      G         F               G                       Am             Em
        Once more you open the door and you're here in my heart,
                    F                 G         Am
        and my heart will go on and on.

Zw.     (Am)   G    F    G

          C                        G                        F             C   G
2.      Love can touch us one time and last for a lifetime,
        C                    G                    F     G7
        and never let go till we're gone.
          C                      G                       F                C     G
        Love was when I loved you; one true time I hold to.
        C                      G              F
        In my life we'll always go on.

Ref.1   Near, far, wherever you are, ...

Zw.     (Am)   G    F    G    Am    G    F    Am  E7

          Am    G                    F             G                  Am                 G                 F    G7
Ref.2   You're here, there's nothing I fear and I know that my heart will go on.
          Am    G        F            G               Am             Em
        We'll stay forever this way. You are safe in my heart,
                    F                 G          C    G    F    G
        and my heart will go on and on.
              C     G       F     C
        Mmh. ---------------------
```


C G F
1.Eve - ry night in my dreams I see you, I

C G C G F G7
feel you, that is how I know you go on.

C G F C G
Far a-cross the dis-tance and spa-ces bet-ween us
C G F Am
you have come to show you go on. Near,
G F G Am
far, wher-e-ver you are, I be-lieve that the
G F G7 Am G
heart does go on. Once more you
F G Am Em
o-pen the door and you're here in my heart, and my
F G Am
heart will go on and on.
1.
G F
G
2.
G F G Am
G F Am E7
D.S.al
G C
on and on.
G F G C G F C
Mmh.

NIGHTS IN WHITE SATIN

♩.	52	Slow Rock

Em **D** **Em** **D**
1. Nights in white satin never reaching the end,
C **G** **F** **Em**
letters I've written never meaning to send.
D **Em** **D**
Beauty I'd always missed with these eyes before,
C **G** **F** **Em**
just what the truth is I can't say anymore.
A **C** **Em** **D** **Em** **D**
Cause I love you. Yes I love you, oh, how I love you, -- oh!

Em **D** **Em** **D**
2. Gazing at people some hand in hand,
C **G** **F** **Em**
just what I'm going through they can't understand.
D **Em** **D**
Some try to tell me thoughts they cannot defend,
C **G** **F** **Em**
just what you want to be, you'll be in the end.
A **C** **Em** **D** **Em** **D** **Em**
And I love you, yes I love you, oh, how I love you, --- oh, how I love you.

Zw. **(Em) D C B Em D C B Em C Em C Am B Am B Em D C Em D Em D**

Em **D** **A**
1. Nights in white satin ... ... Cause I love you.
C **Em** **D** **Em** **D** **Em**
Yes I love you, oh, how I love you, -- oh, how I love you.

Zw. **(Em) D C B Em** ... ... *(fade out)*

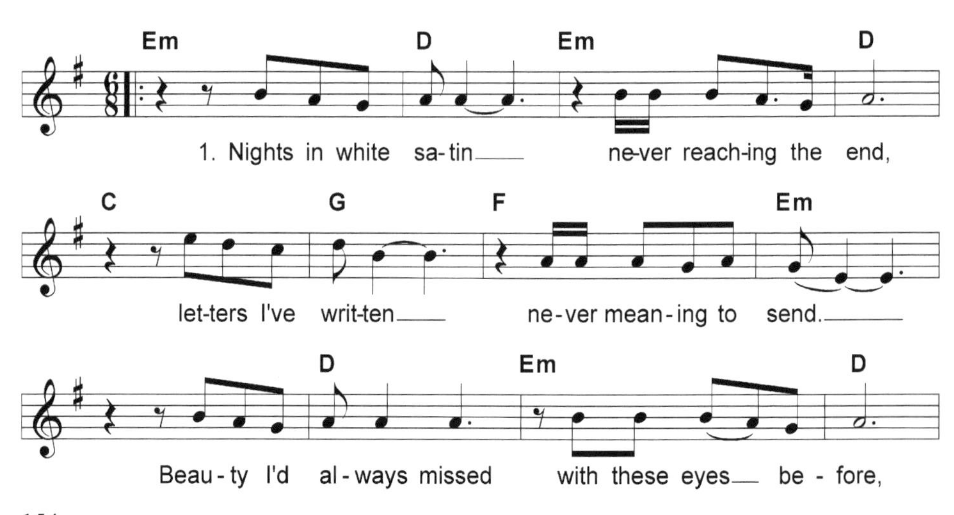

C
G
F
just what the truth is
I can't say a - ny -
Em
A
C
more. Cause I love you.
Yes I love you,
Em
D
1. Em
D
oh, how I love you,
oh!
2. Em
D
Em
Em
oh, how I love you,
D
C
B
Em
D
C
B
Em
C
Em
C
Am
B
Am
B
Em
D
C
Em
D
Em
D
D.C. (ohne Wdhl., dann fade out im Instrumentalteil)

PICTURE

♩	98	Country Beat

```
         G
1.       I'm livin' my life in a slow hell.
                C
         Different girl every night at the hotel.
         D                           C       G
           I ain't seen the sun shining    three damn days.

         Been fuelin' up on (cocain) and whiskey.
           C
         I wish I had a good girl to miss me.
         D                           C       G
           Lord, I wonder if I'll ever    change my ways.

           D        Em                          G
Ref.1    I put your picture away, sat down and cried today.
               D                   C        G
         I can't look at you while I'm lying next to her.
           D        Em                          G
         I put your picture away, sat down and cried today.
               D                 C          G
         I can't look at you why I'm lying next to her.

           G
2.       I called you last night in the hotel.
         C
         Everyone knows but they won't tell,
                D                                C         G
         but their halfhearted smiles tell me something   just ain't right.

         I been waiting on you for a long time.
          C
         Fueling up on heartaches and cheap wine.
         D                    C        G
         I ain't heard from you in   three damn nights.

           D        Em                       G
Re.2     I put your picture away. I wonder where you been.
               D                   C        G
         I can't look at you while I'm lying next to him.
           D        Em                       G
         I put your picture away, I wonder where you been.
               D                   C        G
         I can't look at you while I'm lying next to him.

           G
3.       I saw you yesterday with an old friend,
                 C
         it was the same old same "How have you been?"
         D                                      C         G
           Since you've been gone my world's been    dark and grey.

         You reminded me of brighter days.
           C
         I hoped you were coming home to stay.
```

D C G
I was headed to church, I was off to drink you away.
C
I thought about you for a long time, can't seem to get you of my mind.
D C G
I can't understand why we're living. life this way.

D Em G
Ref.3 I found your picture today. I swear I'll change my ways.
D C G
I just called to say I want you to come back home.
D C C
I just called to say I love you come back home.

C
wish I had a good girl to miss me.
D C G
Lord, I won-der if I'll e - ver change my ways.
D Em
I put your pic-ture a-way, sat down and
G D
cried to-day. I can't look at you while I'm
C 1. G D
ly - ing next to her. I put your
2. G
her. 2.I
2x D.S.(2.mal al Coda)
G D
(3.)home. I just called to say I love
C G
you come back home.

MORE THAN WORDS

♩	94	Slow Bossa

F Bb Gm Bb C F
1. Saying I love you is not the words I want to hear from you,
Bb Gm Bb C Dm
it's not that I want you, not to say, but if you only knew.
Gm C7 F C Dm
How easy it would be to show me how you feel.
Gm C7 F7 Bb
More than words is all you have to do to make it real.
Bbm F Dm Gm C7 Bb⁰ F
Then you wouldn't have to say that you love me, 'cos I'd already know.

C Dm C Bb
Ref. What would you do if my heart was torn in two?
F Gm C7 F
More than words to show you feel that your love for me is real.
C Dm C Bb
What would you say if I took those words away?
F Gm C7 F Bb
Then you couldn't make things new, just by saying I love you. --
Gm Bb C7 F Bb Gm C7
La la la la la la la. More than words.La la la la la la.

F Bb Gm Bb C F
2. Now that I've tried to talk to you and make you understand,
Bb Gm Bb C Dm
all you have to do is close your eyes and just reach out your hands
Gm C7 F C Dm
and touch me. Hold me close don't ever let me go!
Gm C7 F7 Bb
More than words is all I ever needed you to show,
Bbm F Dm Gm C7 Bb⁰ F
Then you wouldn't have to say that you love me, 'cos I'd already know.
Bb Gm Bb C7 F
//: La la la la la la la la la la la. More than words. ://

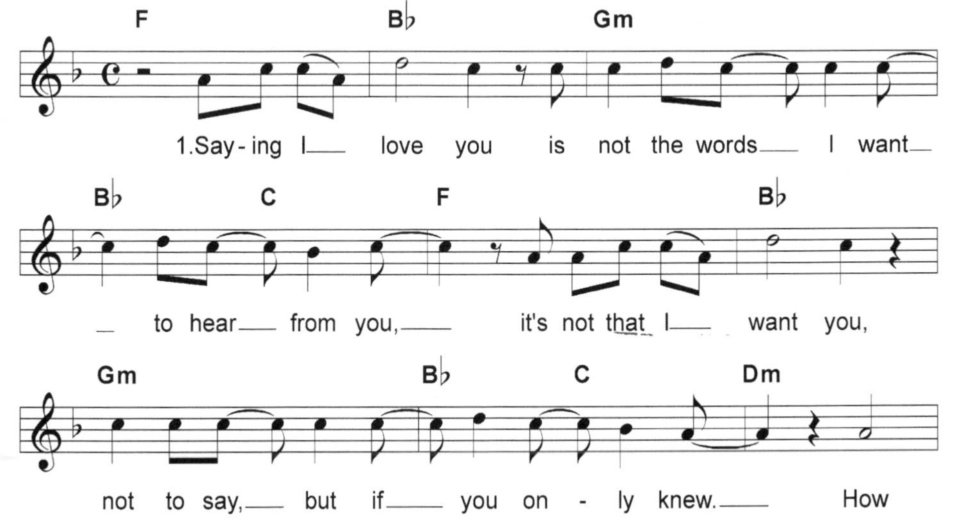

Gm C7 F C
ea - sy it would be to show me how you feel.
Dm Gm C7
More than words is all you have to do
F7 B♭
to make it real. Then you would -
B♭m F Dm
- n't have to say that you love me, 'cos
Gm C7 B♭° F
I'd al - rea - dy know. What would you do
C Dm C B♭
if my heart was torn in two? More than words
F Gm
to show you feel that your love
C7 F
for me is real. What would you say

C
Dm
C
_ if I took_ those words_ a - way?_
B♭
F
_ Then you could - n't make_ things new,_
Gm
C7
F
B♭
_ just by say - ing I love_ you._ La la la_
Gm
B♭
C7
F
_ la la_ la la._ More_ than words._
B♭
Gm
C7
F
D.C.al Coda
La la la la_ la la la._
know.
B♭
Gm
La la la la_ la la la_ la la_ la la._
B♭
C7
F
B♭
_ More_ than words._ La la la la_ la la la_
Gm
B♭
C7
F
_ la la_ la la._ More_ than words._

PERFEKTE WELLE

♩	112	Pop Beat

1.

Em C
Mit jeder Welle kam ein Traum, doch Träume geh'n vorüber.
Em C
Dein Brett ist verstaubt, deine Zweifel schäumen über.
Am D
Du hast dein Leben lang gewartet, hast gehofft, dass es sie gibt.
C
Hast den Glauben fast verloren, hast dich nicht vom Fleck bewegt.
Am C
Jetzt kommt sie langsam auf dich zu, das Wasser schlägt dir ins Gesicht.
Am C
Du siehst dein Leben wie ein' Film, du kannst nicht glauben, dass sie bricht.

Ref.

Em C
Das ist die perfekte Welle, das ist der perfekte Tag.
Am C
Lass dich einfach von ihr tragen, denk am besten gar nicht nach.
Em C
Das ist die perfekte Welle, das ist der perfekte Tag.
Am Cj7
Es gibt mehr als du weißt, es gibt mehr als du sagst.

2.

Em C
Deine Hände sind schon taub, hast Salz in deinen Augen.
Em C
Zwischen Tränen und Staub, fällt es schwer noch dran zu glauben.
Am D
Du hast dein Leben lang gewartet, hast die Wellen nie gezählt,
C
hast das alles nicht gewollt, du hast viel zu schnell gelebt.
Am C
Jetzt kommt sie langsam auf dich zu, das Wasser schlägt dir ins Gesicht.
Am C
Du siehst dein Leben wie ein' Film, du kannst nicht glauben, dass sie bricht.

Ref.

Em C D
Das ist die perfekte Welle, ... es gibt mehr als du sagst.

Br.

C D Am Em
Du stellst dich in den Sturm und schreist: "Ich bin hier, ich bin frei!
C D Am
Alles was ich will ist Zeit! Ich bin hier, ich bin frei!"
C D Am Em
Du stellst dich in den Sturm und schreist: "Ich bin hier, ich bin frei,
C D
ich bin hier, ich bin frei!"

Zw.

Em C D Am Em C D Am Em
Das ist die perfekte Welle.

C D Em C D Em C D Em C D Em C D Em C D

Ref.

Em C
Das ist die perfekte Welle, ... es gibt mehr als du sagst.

Em G Am
Das ist die perfekte Welle, das ist der perfekte Tag dafür.
C Em G Am C Em
Das ist die perfekte Welle, -------- das ist der perfekte Tag.

Em
1.Mit je - der Wel - le kam ein Traum, doch Träu - me geh'n vor -
C
Em
ü - ber. Dein Brett ist ver - staubt, dei - ne Zwei - fel schäu - men
C
ü - ber. Du hast dein Le - ben lang ge -
Am
D
war - tet, hast ge - hofft, dass es sie gibt. Hast den Glau - ben fast ver -
C
lo - ren, hast dich nicht vom Fleck be - wegt.
Am
Jetzt kommt sie lang - sam auf dich zu, das Was - ser schlägt dir ins Ge -
C
sicht. Du siehst dein Le - ben wie ein'
Am
C
Film, du kannst nicht glau - ben, dass sie bricht. Das ist die per - fek - te
Em
C
Wel - le, das ist der per - fek - te Tag. Lass dich ein - fach von ihr

Am
C
tra - gen, denk am bes - ten gar nicht nach. Das ist die per - fek - te
Em
C
1&2
Wel - le, das ist der per - fek - te Tag. Es gibt mehr als du
Am
CMaj7
weißt, es gibt mehr als du sagst.
2.Dei - ne Hän - de sind schon
D.S.al 1
1
Am
C
D
weißt, es gibt mehr als du sagst. Du
C
D
Am
Em
stellst dich in den Sturm und schreist: "Ich bin hier, ich bin frei!
C
D
Am
Al - les was ich will ist Zeit! Ich bin hier, ich bin frei!" Du
C
D
Am
Em
stellst dich in den Sturm und schreist: "Ich bin hier, ich bin frei,
C
D
Em
C
ich bin hier, ich bin frei!"

D Am Em C D Am Em C
Das ist die per-fek-te Wel-le.
D Em C D Em C
D Em C D Em C
D Em C D
D.S.al 𝄌2
Das ist die per-fek-te
Am C
weißt, es gibt mehr als du sagst. Das ist die per-fek-te
Em G Am
Wel-le, das ist der per-fek-te Tag da-für.
3
C Em G
Das ist die per-fek-te Wel-le,
Am C Em
das ist der per-fek-te Tag.

PLEASE MR. POSTMAN

♩	123	Rock-Beat

```
         Em     G                                      Em                  G
Intro    Wait! Oh yes, wait a minute Mister Postman,      wait Mister Postman.

         G                            Em
Ref.       Mister Postman look and see,      if there's a letter in the bag for me.
         C                                  D                         D7
           I've been waiting a long long time,   since I heard from that gal of mine.

         G                             D Em
1.         There must be some mail today --     from my girlfriend so far away.
         C                                     D                      D7
           Please Mister Postman look and see,     if there's a letter, a letter for me.

         G                                          D   Em
2.         I've been standing here waiting Mister Postman      so patiently,
         C                               D                          D7
           for just a card or just a letter,    saying she's returning home to me.

Ref.     Mister Postman look and see, ...

         G                              D Em
3.         So many days you past me by, --     saw the tears standing in my eye.
         C                                          D                     D7
           You didn't stop to make me feel better,     by leaving me a card or a letter.

Ref.     Mister Postman look and see, ...

                         G                                           D
Br.      //: You gotta wait a minute, wait a minute, oh yeah!
           Em
         Wait a minute, wait a minute, oh yeah!
                       C
         You gotta wait a minute, wait a minute, oh yeah!
            D
         Check it and see one more time for me!
                       G                                        D
         You gotta wait a minute, wait a minute, oh yeah!
           Em
         Wait a minute, wait a minute, oh yeah!
                  C
         Mister Postman, oh yeah!
            D
         Deliver the letter, the sooner the better! ://     (fade out)
```

Words & Music by Brian Holland, Freddie Gorman, Robert Bateman, Georgia Dobbins & William Garrett

Em G Em
Wait! Oh yes, wait a mi-nute Mis-ter Post-man, wait
G G
Mis-ter Post - man. Mis-ter Post-man look and see,
Em
if there's a let - ter in the bag for me.
C
I've been wait - ing a long long time,
D D7
since I heard from that gal of mine.
G D
1.There must be some mail to - day
Em
from my girl - friend so far a - way.
C
Please Mis - ter Post - man look and see,
D D7
if there's a let - ter, a let - ter for me.

G D Em
2.I've been standing here waiting Mister Postman so
C
patient - ly, for just a card or just a let-ter,
D D7 G
saying she's re-turning home to me. Mis-ter Post-man
Em
look and see, if there's a let-ter in the bag for me.
C
I've been wait - ing a long long time,
D D7
since I heard from that gal of mine.
G D
3.So ma - ny days you past me by,
Em C
saw the tears stand-ing in my eye. You did-n't stop to
D
make me feel bet - ter, by leav - ing me a

D7
D.S.al Coda
D7
card or a let - ter.
gal of mine. You got - ta
G
D
wait a mi - nute, wait a mi - nute, oh yeah!
Em
Wait a mi - nute, wait a mi - nute, oh yeah! You got - ta
C
wait a mi - nute, wait a mi - nute, oh yeah!
D
Check it and see one more time for me! You got - ta
G
D
wait a mi - nute, wait a mi - nute, oh yeah!
Em
Wait a mi - nute, wait a mi - nute, oh yeah! Mis - ter
C
Post - man, oh yeah! De -
D
fade out
liv - er the let - ter, the soon - er the bet - ter! Got - ta

QUINN THE ESKIMO
(The Mighty Quinn)

♩	93	Rock-Beat

```
           G                   D          G
Ref.  //: Come all without, come all within,
                     Bm              C      G        (G C7 G C7)
      you'll not see nothing like the Mighty Quinn. ://

      G              C7        G         C7
1.       Everybody's building ships and boats.
      G                          C7        G                C7
         Some are building monuments, others jotting down notes.
      G             C7           G                 C7
         Everybody's in despair,      every girl and boy,
                 G                     D
      but when Quinn, the Eskimo, gets here,
            C7                     G
      everybody's gonna jump for joy.

Ref.  Come all without, ...

        G                C7              G                C7
2.    I like to do just like the rest, I like my sugar sweet,
          G                          C7               G                C7
      but jumping queues and making haste, it ain't my cup of meat.
      G                C7                      G          C7
         Everyone's beneath the trees, feeding pigeons on a limb,
                 G                     D
      but when Quinn, the Eskimo, gets here,
              C7                   G
      all the pigeons gonna run to him.

Ref.  //: Come all without, come all within, ...

      G                        C7         G              C7
3.       Let me do what I wanna do, I can recite them all,
           G                   C7        G                C7
      just tell me where it hurts and I'll tell you who to call.
      G                C7                  G                       C7
         Nobody can get no sleep, there's someone on everyone's toes,
                 G                     D
      but when Quinn, the Eskimo, gets here,
           C7                       G
      everybody's gonna wanna doze.

Ref.  //: Come all without, come all within, ... :// (fade out)
```

Words & Music by Bob Dylan

G
D
G
Come all with-out, come all with-in, you'll
Bm
C
G
not see noth-ing like the Migh-ty Quinn.
G
C7
G
C7
G
C7
G
C7
1.Eve-ry-bo-dy's build-ing ships and boats.
G
C7
Some are build-ing mo-nu-ments,
G
C7
G
C7
o-thers jot-ting down notes. Eve-ry-bo-dy's in des-pair,
G
C7
eve-ry girl and boy, but when
G
D
Quinn, the Es-ki-mo, gets here, eve-ry-
C7
G
D.C. (fade out im Refrain)
bo-dy's gon-na jump for joy.

RADIO ORCHID

♩	85	Hard Rock

```
       Am                  F      G
1.     There's an old lady,     living in an old house,
                  Am                 F         G
       since her husband died she hasn't been out.
          Am                F                G
       She lives in her own world with her own little nightmares
       Am            F                       G     Am  F G   Am  F G
            and she stopped counting the days.

                    Am            F              G
2.     She buys a radio station     with her husbands legacy,
                      Am               F     G
       she does her own show ten hours a day.
             Am                 F        G
       Plays poems and listens    lets feelings run free,
              Am                F      G
       helps people talk their pain away.

       B♭                                      Dm
Zw.         So if your world falls down, can't see the light of day,
                C                         G     B♭
       call the lady, call the station today and...

       Am            F     G                      Am F        G                          Am
Ref.        This is Radio Orchid, listen and cry to all the others that suffer and die.
                F    G                       Am
       This is Radio Orchid, listen and cry,
                  F                    G        (Am  F G   Am   F G)
       take your lonely heart and let it fly.

         Am                       F        G
3.     Sending her message,          she's solving the problems
           Am                        F        G
       of millions and millions        and who solves hers?
              Am                     F        G
       The old lady gets older,        still lives in her old house,
                       Am            F          G
       but when she dies we'll all live alone.

Zw.    So if your world falls down, ...

Ref.   This is Radio Orchid, ...

       Am F  G                                   Am          F G
Zw.                  Take your lonely heart and let it fly!

Zw.    So if your world falls down, ...

Ref.   This is Radio Orchid, ...          (fade out)
```

Words by Kai-Uwe Wingenfelder
Music by Thorsten Wingenfelder & Jens Krause

Am
F
G
1.There's an old la-dy, liv-ing in an old house, since her
hus-band died she has-n't been out. She
lives in her own world with her own lit-tle night-mares
and she stopped count-ing the days.
2.She buys a
ra-di-o sta-tion with her hus-bands le-ga-cy, she does her
own show ten hours a day. Plays
poems and list-ens lets feel-ings run free, helps

Am F G
peo - ple talk their pain a - way.
B♭ Dm
So if your world falls down, can't see the light of day, call the la -
C G B♭
- dy, call the sta-tion to-day and...
Am F G Am F
This is Ra-di - o Or - chid, list-en and cry to all the o -
G Am F
- thers that suf - fer and die. This is Ra - di - o Or -
G Am F
- chid, list - en and cry, take your lone - ly heart and
G Am F G
let it fly. Take your lone - ly heart and
Am F G
let it fly!
D.S. (fade out im Refrain)

REDEMPTION SONG

♩	118	Folk

Intro **G C G C D G C G C D G**

```
        G                   Em       C          G         Am
1.      Old pirates, yes, they rob I. Sold I to the merchant ships
        G                      Em   C             G         Am
          minutes after they took I    from the bottomless pit.
              G          Em          C           G              Am
        But my hand was made strong     by the hand of the Almighty.
           G                       Em   C                D
        We forward in this generation      triumphantly.

                               G    C          D       G
Ref.    Won't you help to sing        these songs of freedom?
                 C    D    Em  C      D          G      C      D           G     (C  D)
        'Cause all I ever had,        redemption songs,       redemption songs.

              G                             Em
2.      Emancipate yourselves from mental slavery,
                      C          G       Am
        none but ourselves can free our minds.
               G               Em                       C        G       Am
        Have no fear for atomic energy, 'cause none of them can stop the time.
            G                         Em                 C     G         Am
        How long shall they kill our prophets while we stand aside and look?
              G             Em               C                D
        Some say it's just a part of it. We've got to fulfill the book.

Ref.    Won't you help to sing ...

        C     D          G
          redemption songs.

Zw.     C D  Em   C D Em   C D Em   C D Em   C D

2.      Emancipate yourselves ...

                               G    C    C      D        G
Ref.    Won't you help to sing ... ...      redemption songs.

        C   D    Em C      D         Em
        All I ever had,       redemption songs.
        C        D        G        C  D          G        C  G  Am    D7
          These songs of freedom,       songs of freedom.
```

Words & Music by Bob Marley

1.Old pi - rates, yes, they rob I. Sold
I to the mer - chant ships min - utes af - ter they took
I from the bot - tom - less pit. But my
hand was made strong by the hand of the Al -
migh - ty. We for - ward in this ge - ne - ra - tion
tri - um-phant - ly. Won't you help to sing
these songs of free - dom? 'Cause all I e - ver had,

Em C D G C D
re - demp - tion songs, re - demp - tion
1. G C D 2. G C D
songs. 2.E - man - ci - songs. re - demp - tion
G C D Em C D Em C D
songs.
D.S.al
Em C D Em C D G
2.E - man - ci - songs.
C D Em C D Em
All I e - ver had, re - demp - tion songs.
C D G C D G C G
These songs of free - dom, songs of free - dom.
Am D7

RESCUE ME

♩	72	Pop Ballad

```
                      G
1.     Yeah, and I wanna have the time and I wanna see you cry,

       I wanna feel your body and I wanna get closer.
             C
       Gotta rescue me, rescue me, rescue me, let me have a good time.
              G
       And I wanna see you laughin' and I wanna feel rain,

       I wanna get inside you and I wanna feel pain.
                 C
       You gotta rescue me, rescue me, rescue me, let me have a good time.
              D
       And I wanna feel you movin' and I wanna feel good,
         C
       I wanna feel your love for sure.

         G       Am      D
Ref.   Let your, let your, let your amazement grow.
         G       Am      D
       Let your, let your, let your amazement grow.
       G                    Am    D
          Oh whatever you do,--   I can't leave you.
                         Am D              G
       Don't ever let me go,    dont ever let me go.

                      G
2.     Yeah, and I wanna be hungry and I wanna ask why,

       I wanna be dreaming and I wanna satisfy.
            C
       You gotta rescue me, rescue me, rescue me, let me have a good time.
              G
       And I wanna be love it and I wanna be high,

       I wanna feel you touch me and I wanna hear you sigh.
                 C
       You gotta rescue me, rescue me, rescue me, let me have a good time.
              D
       And I wanna feel you movin and I wanna feel good,
         C
       I wanna feel your love for sure.

         G       Am            D                   Gm G2 Gm G2 G2/D
Ref.   Let your, let your, ...  ...  dont ever let me go.

        G
Zw.    Let your! Let your! Let your! Let your! Let your! Let your!

         G       Am                                      G Am D
Ref.   Let your, let your, ...  ...  leave you. Dont ever let me go,
                         Gm
       dont ever let me go.
```

Musik: Hendrik Röder, Andreas Birr
Text: Jana Gross, Andreas Birr, William Lennoy

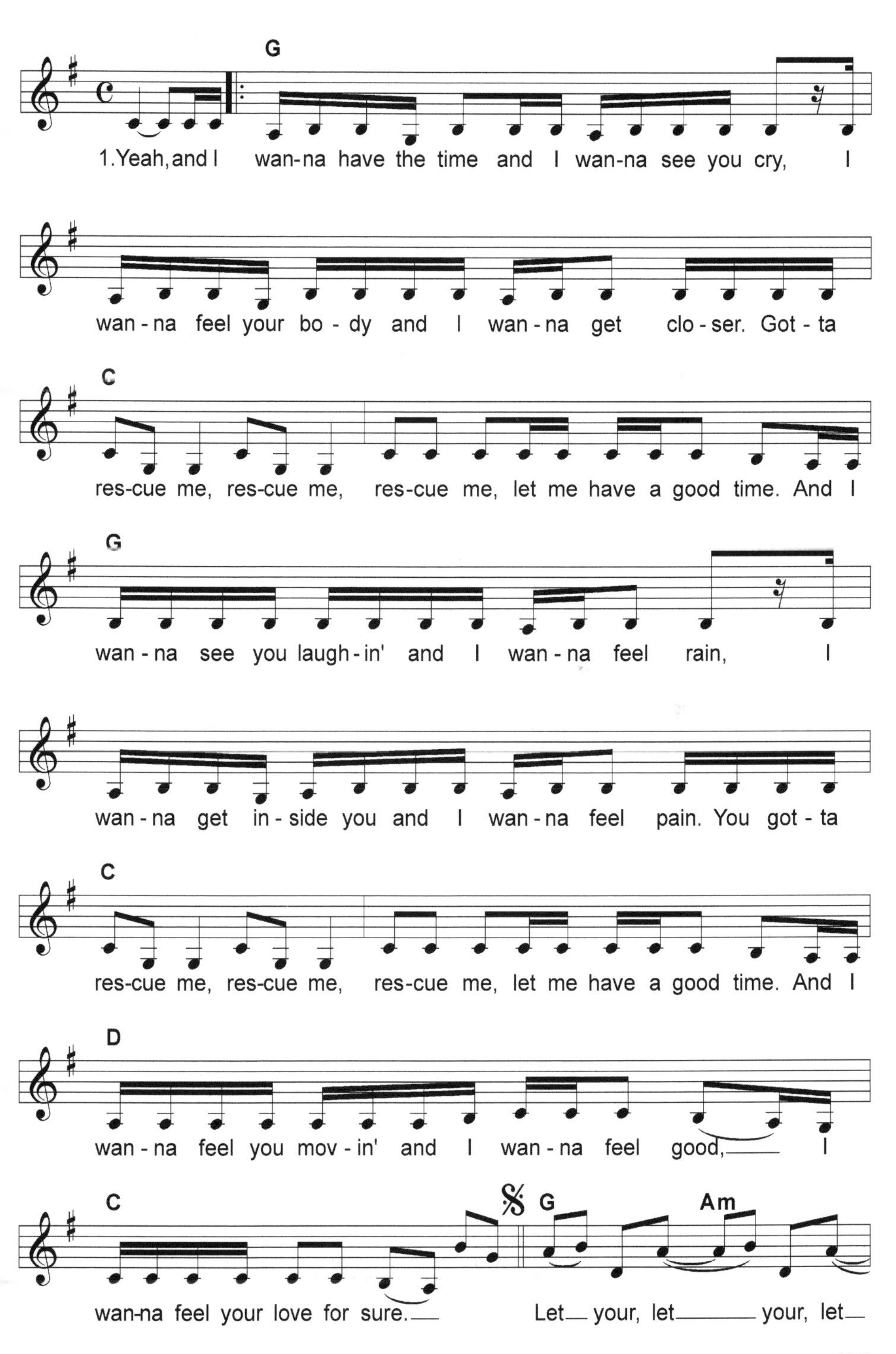
G
1.Yeah, and I wan-na have the time and I wan-na see you cry, I
wan - na feel your bo - dy and I wan - na get clo - ser. Got - ta
C
res-cue me, res-cue me, res-cue me, let me have a good time. And I
G
wan - na see you laugh - in' and I wan - na feel rain, I
wan - na get in - side you and I wan - na feel pain. You got - ta
C
res-cue me, res-cue me, res-cue me, let me have a good time. And I
D
wan - na feel you mov - in' and I wan - na feel good, I
C
wan-na feel your love for sure.
G
Am
Let your, let your, let

D
G
Am
your a-maze - ment grow. Let your, let your, let
D
G
Am
your a-maze - ment grow. Oh what-e-ver you do, I can't
D
Am
leave you. Don't e - ver let me go,
D
1.
G
dont e-ver let me go. 2.Yeah, and I
2.
Gm
Gsus2
Gm
go.
Gsus2
Gsus2/D
G
Let your! Let your! Let
your! Let your! Let your! Let your!
D.S.al Coda
G
Am
D
Gm
go, dont e-ver let me go.

ROCKING ON HEAVENS FLOOR

♩	125	Rock

A G D A G D
1. Can't wait sittin' in the blocks, I can see the daylight.
A G D A
Let's go, startin' up the show, flashes hit me so bright.
F C F Am B♭
When the clouds go by try to satisfy. Come on now!

A G D A
Ref. Rockin' on heaven's floor, get the angels freakin' more an more.
G D A
Rockin' on heaven's floor, devil's only knockin' right out there on the door.

A G D A G D
2. Can't stop livin on the edge, had to be a hero.
A G D A
Be strong, banging all night long, counting down to zero.
F C F Am B♭
When the clouds go by try to satisfy. Come on now! *Ref. ...*

Zw. Come on!
A G D A
Oh, oh, oh, oh, oh, Baby! Oh, oh, oh, oh!
G D A
Oh, oh, oh, oh, oh, Baby! Oh, oh, oh, oh! Come on now!
A D A G A D A G D G A
Oh!

F C F Am B♭
Zw. When the clouds go by try to satisfy. Come on now! *Ref. ...*

(A) G D A
Yeah! Yeah! Yeah! Oh, yeah!
G D A
Oh, oh, oh, oh, oh, Baby! Oh, oh, oh, oh!
G D A
Oh, oh, oh, oh, oh, Baby! Oh, oh, oh, oh

Rockin' on heavens floor!

F
- es hit me so bright. When the
C F Am B♭
clouds go by try to sa - tis - fy.
A
Come on now! Rock - in' on hea - vens floor, get
G D A
the an-gels freak - in more an more. Rock - in' on hea -
G D
- vens floor, de - vil's on-ly knock-in right out there on the
A
door.
1.
2.
Come on!
A G
Oh, oh, oh, oh, oh, Ba-by! Oh, oh, oh, oh!
D A
Oh, oh, oh, oh, oh, Ba-by! Oh,

Musik: Frank Johnes/Thomas Remm/Bodybrain Text: Wonderbra

ROCKIN ALL OVER THE WORLD

♩	131	Hard Rock

```
        C
1.         Hurry up, hurry up, here we go,
        F7
           all aboard 'caus we're hittin' the road
                   C  G7                       C
        here we go rockin' all over the world!

        C
2.         Gittyup, Gittyup get away,
          F7
        we're goin' crazy and we're goin' today
                   C  G7                       C
        here we go rockin' all over the world!

               C                                F7
Ref.    And I like it, I like it, I like it, I like it, I lalala like it lalalali
                    C  G7                      C
        here we go rockin' all over the world!

4.      C      F7       C    G7    C       (Instrumental)

5.      C      F7       C    G7    C       (Instrumental)

              C
6.      I'm gonna tell your mama what you're gonna do,
         F7
        just come out tonight with your rockin' shoes
                    C G7                       C
        here we go rockin' all over the world!

Ref.    And I like it, ... (Wdhl. nach Belieben, fade out)
```

Words & Music by John Fogerty

C
1.Hur - ry up, hur - ry up, here we go,
F7
C
all a - board 'caus we're hitt - in' the road here we go
G7
C
rock - in' all o - ver the world!
C
2.Git - ty - up, Git - ty - up get a - way,
F7
we're go - in' cra - zy and we're go - in' to - day here we go
C
G7
C
rock - in' all o - ver the world!
C
And I like it, I like it, I like it, I like it, I la -
F7
C
- la - la like it la - la - la - li here we go
G7
C
D.C.
rock - in' all o - ver the world!

ROCK'N ROLL - I GAVE YOU THE BEST YEARS OF MY LIFE

♩	96	Folk

```
        C                                  F                      G
1.         I can still remember when I      bought my first guitar,
                    C                                              F                G
        remember     just how good the feeling was, put it proudly in my car.
                  C                                        A7              Dm
        And my family listened fifty times to my two-song repertoire,
                                                   F          G     C
        and I told my mum her only son was      gonna be a star.
                                           F                         G
        Bought all the Beatle records,      sounded just like Paul,
          C                                   F                          G
        bought all the old Chuck Berry's,      seventy-eight's and all.
               C                                  A7                    Dm
        And I sat by my record player, playin' every note they played,
                                                  F        G           C
        and I watched them all on TV, makin every move they made.

        C                      C7                F
Ref.1      Rock and roll, I gave you all the best years of my life,
                    G                               F                C
        all the dreamy sunny Sundays, all the moon-lit summer nights.
                                  C7               F
        I was so busy in the back room writin' love songs to you,
                           G                                       F            C
        while you were changin' your direction, and you never even knew,
                    G7                         C
        that I was always just one step behind you.

        C                                          F          G
2.         Sixty-six seemed like the year I was really goin' somewhere,
                   C                                 F                G
        we were living in San Francisco, with flowers in our hair.
        C                                        A7                  Dm
           Singing songs of kindness so the world would understand,
                                                                F      G       C
        but the guys and me were something more than just another band.
                                       F                      G
        And then sixty-nine in L.A.,        came around so soon,
                    C                               F              G
        we were really making headway and writing lots of tunes.
                    C                                    A7                    Dm
        And we must have played the wildest stuff        we had ever played,
                                                      F            G      C
        the way the crowds cried out for us, we thought we had it made.

        C                      C7                F
Ref.2      Rock and roll, I gave you all the best years of my life,
                   G                              F            C
        all the crazy lazy young days, all the magic moon-lit nights.
                                  C7          F
        I was so busy on the road, singin' love songs to you,
                           G                                       F            C
        while you were changin' your direction, and you never even knew,
                    G7                         C
        that I was always just one step behind you.
```

Zw. **C F G C F G C**

C F G
3. Seventy-one in Soho, when I saw Suzanne,
C F G
I was trying to go it solo, with someone else's band.
C A7 Dm
And she came up to me later and I took her by the hand.
F G C
And I told her all my troubles and she seemed to understand.
F G
And she followed me through London, through a hundred hotel rooms,
C F G
through a hundred record companies who didn't like my tunes.
C A7 Dm
And she followed me when, finally, I sold my old guitar,
F G C
and she tried to help me understand, I'd never be a star.

C C7 F
Ref.3 Rock and roll, I gave you all the best years of my life,
G F C
all the dreamy sunny Sundays, all the moon-lit summer nights.
C7 F
And though I never knew the magic of makin' it with you,
G F C
thank the Lord for giving me the little bit I knew.
G7 C
And I will always be one step behind you.

C C7 F
Ref.4 Rock and roll, I gave you all the best years of my life,
G F C
singing out my love songs in the brightly flashing lights.
C7 F
And though I never knew the magic of makin' it with you,
G F C
thank the Lord for giving me the little bit I knew.

Ref.3 *fade out*

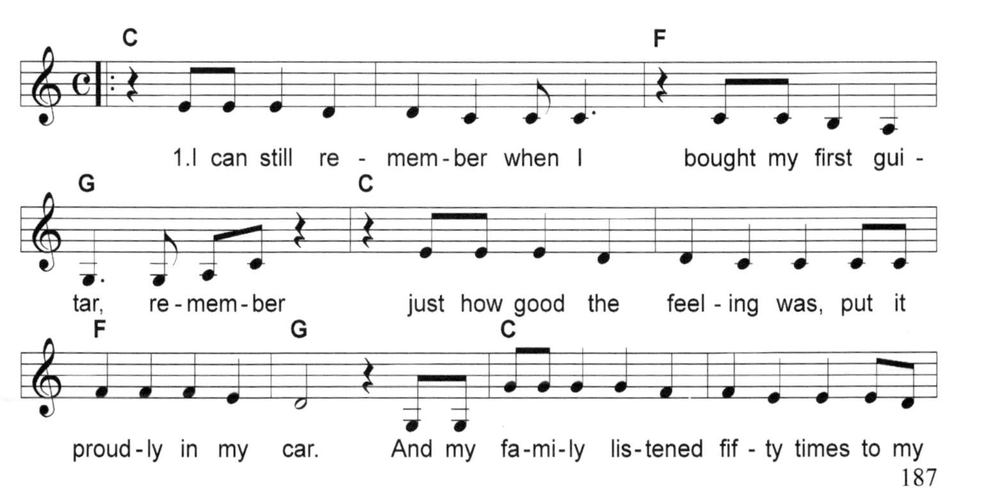

Words & Music by Kevin Johnson

SEXED UP

♩ 76 | 8 Beat

C F Am Em
1. Loose lips on ships, I'm getting to grips with what you said.
C F Am G
Know it's not in my head I can't awake and forget day after day.
F
Why don't we talk about it?
G E Am
Why do you always doubt that there can be a better way?
Dm G
It doesn't make me want to stay.

C Em F G
Ref. Why don't we break up, there's nothing left to say.
C Em F G
I got my eye shut, praying they won't stray.
C E F Fm
And we're not sexed up, that's what makes the difference today.
C (Em F G C Em F G)
I hope you blow away.

C F Am Em
2. You said we're fatally flawed when I'm easily bored. Is that okay?
C F Am G
Strike me off your list, make this the last kiss, I'll walk away.
F
Why don't we talk about it?
G E Am
I'm only here don't shout it given time we'll forget.
Dm G
Let's pretend we never met!

Ref. Why don't we break up, ...

F G Em Am F G
Screw you, I didn't like your taste anyway, I chose you.
Em Am B♭ F Fm
Let's all gone to wasted Saturday, I'll go out and find another you.
C Em F G C Em F G
Why don't we, ...

Ref. Why don't we break up, ...

Gm C Gm C
I hope you blow away. I hope you blow away.
Gm C Gm C
Away. Blow away. Away.

Words and Music by Robert Williams and Guy Chambers

C F
1.Loose lips on ships, I'm get - ting to grips
Am Em C
with what you said. Know it's not in my head
F Am G
I can't a - wake and for - get day af - ter day.
F G
Why don't we talk a - bout it? Why do you al - ways doubt that
E Am
there can be a bet - ter way? It
Dm G
does - n't make me want to stay. Why don't we
C Em F G C Em
break up, there's noth - ing left to say. I got my eye shut,
F G C E
pray - ing they won't stray. And we're not sexed up,
F Fm
that's what makes the diffe - rence to - day. I hope you blow a -
C Em F G C Em F G
way.
D.C.al Coda

C F G Em Am
way. Screw you, I did-n't like your taste a-ny-way,
F G Em Am B♭
I chose you. Let's all gone to wast-ed Sa-tur-day, I'll go
F Fm
out and find an - oth - er you.
C Em F G C Em F G
Why don't wc, ... Why don't we
C Em F G C Em
break up, there's noth-ing left to say. I got my eye shut,
F G C E
pray - ing they won't stray. And we're not sexed up,
F Fm
that's what makes the diffe-rence to-day. I hope you blow a -
C Gm C
way. I hope you blow a - way.
Gm C
I hope you blow a - way. A -
Gm C Gm C
way. Blow a - way. A - way.

SHOULD I STAY OR SHOULD I GO

♩	112	Rock

```
     D                                  G  D                              G  D
1.      Darling you got to let me know       should I stay or should I go?
                               G    F G                              D    G D
     If you say that you are mine,        I'll be here 'till the end of time.
                         A7                                   D  G
     So you got to let know should I stay or should I go?

     D                                 G  D                                     G  D
2.      It's always tease tease tease,       you're happy when I'm on my knees.
                                   G    F G                               D   G D
     One day is fine and next is black,       so if you want me off your back.
                                A7                                D  G
     Well come on and let me know should I Stay or should I go?

                                          G D
Ref. Should I stay or should I go now?
                                          G D
     Should I stay or should I go now?
                            G     F  G                            D     G D
     If I go there will be trouble       and if I stay it will be double.
                                A7
     So come on and let me know.

     D                                  G  D                                 G  D
3.      This indecision's bugging me,        if you don't want me, set me free.
                                        G F G
     Exactly who'm I'm supposed to be,
                                          D      G D
     don't you know which clothes even fit me?
                             A7                                  D  G
     Come on and let me know should I Stay or should I go?
```

4. *Instrumental*

Ref. Should I stay or should I go now? ...

Ref. Should I stay or should I go now? ... *(fade out)*

Words & Music by Joe Strummer & Mick Jones

D G
1.Dar - ling you got to let me know
D G D
should I stay or should I go? If you say that you are
G F G D G
mine, I'll be here 'till the end of time.
D A7
So you got to let me know should I stay or should I
D G D G
go? Should I stay or should I go now?
D G
Should I stay or should I go now?
D G F G
If I go there will be trou - ble and if I stay it will be
D G D A7
dou - ble. So come on and let me know.
D.C. (fade out im Refrain)

SITTIN' ON THE DOCK OF THE BAY

♩	104	Rhythm & Blues

```
       G                      B          C                         A7
1.     Sittin' in the morning sun, I'll be sittin', when the evenin' come,
        G                     B          C                      A7
       watchin' the ships roll in. Then I watch 'em roll away again. Yeah!
       G                           E               G           E
       Sittin' on the dock of the bay watchin' the tide roll away. Uh!
       G                           A7        G      E
       Sittin' on the dock of the bay wastin' time. ----

        G                  B         C                     A7
2.     I left my home in Georgia, headed for the 'Frisco Bay.
            G                     B                    C                     A7
       'Cause I have nothing to live for, looks like nothing gonna come my way.
                         G                           E                G        E
       So I'm just gonna sittin' on the dock of the bay watchin' the tide roll away.
       G                           A7         G      E
       Sittin' on the dock of the bay wastin' time. ----

       G      D   C                     G
Zw.      Look like nothing's gonna change. --
       D           C                G
       Ev'rything still remains the same --
         D               C   G
       I can't do what people tell me to do.
       F                   D
         So I guess I remain the same.

       G                      B             C                       A7
3.     Sittin' here restin' my bones and this loneliness won't leave me alone.
       G                             B          C                 A7
       It's two thousand miles I roam just to make this dock my home.
               G                        E                 G           E
       Now I'm sittin' on the dock of the bay watchin' the tide roll away. Uh!
       G                           A7         G      E
       Sittin' on the dock of the bay wastin' time. ----
```

Outro *(pfeifen:)* **//: G** **E ://** *(fade out)*

Words & Music by Steve Cropper & Otis Redding

G
B
1.Sit - tin' in the mor - ning sun,
I'll be
C
A7
sit - tin', when the eve - nin' come,
G
B
watch - in' the ships roll in.
Then I
C
A7
watch 'em roll a - way a - gain.
Yeah!
G
E
Sit - tin' on the dock of the bay
watch - in' the tide
G
E
G
roll a - way.
Uh! Sit - tin' on the dock of the bay
A7
1.G
E
wast - in' time.
2.I
2.G
E
G
D
time.
Look like

C
G
D
C
noth - ing's gon - na change.
Eve - ry - thing still re - mains the same
G
D
C
G
I can't do what peo - ple tell me to do.
F
D
D.C.al
So I guess I re - main the same.
G
E
G
time.
E
fade out

STRENGTH OF A WOMAN

♩	86	Reggae-Beat

```
      C      F                  G                     F                     C       F G F
1.       So amazing how this world was made, I wonder if God is a woman.
      C            F                G                F                        C       F G F
         The gift of life astounds me to this day,     I give it up for the woman.
      C            F                   G             F            C       F G F
         She's the constant wind that fills my sail, oh, that woman.
               C             F
      With her smile and her style,
                G                 F            C        F G F
      she'll protect you like a child, that's a woman.

                     C     F     G
Ref.  She'll put a smile upon her face
      F             C       F       G
         and take you to that higher place.
      F             C      F     G
        So don't you under estimate
      F                C         F G F                       C       F G (F)
        the strength of a woman,          the strength of a woman.

      C    F              G          F                                C       F G F
2.        Woke up this morning, I got up with the scent of a woman.
      C               F                G
          Just picture if you could what life would be
      F                            C       F G F
      ain't much good without a woman.
      C             F              G               F           C       F G F
         She can nag and be a constant pain, oh, that woman.
                   C                F
      But those hips she's got me whipped
                      G              F            C       F G F
      and it's just to hard to resist, what a woman.

Ref.  She'll put a smile upon her face ...

      F                              G                              F
Br.     Tender lips that's so, so sweet, gentle words she softly speaks.
                                  G                                     F
      Such an angel when we need, God bless the ground beneath her feet.
                                G                              Am
      She can take you on a high, be your comfort when you cry.
                                  F                   G           C        F G
      But if you look into her eyes, you'll see the strength of a woman,
               F          C       F G F
      the strength of a woman.

Ref.  She'll put a smile upon her face ... (fade out)
```

Musik und Text: ORVILLE BURRELL, RICARDO GEORGE DUCENT, MICHAEL GEORGE FLETCHER, CHRISTOPHER S. BIRCH, ROBERT BROWNE, SHAUN DARSON, SHAUN PIZZONIA

C F G F
1.So a-ma - zing how this world was made, I won-der if God is a
C F G F C F
wo-man. The gift of life a-stounds me
G F C F G F
to this day, I give it up for the wo-man.
C F G F
She's the con-stant wind that fills my sail, oh, that
C F G F C F
wo-man. With her smile and her style, she'll pro -
G F C F G F
tect you like a child, that's a wo-man. She'll put a
C F G F
smile up - on her face and take you
C F G F C F
to that high - er place. So don't you un-der es - ti-mate

G F C F G F
— the strength of a wo - man, the strength of a
C F G F G F
1. 2.
wo - man.__ Ten-der lips that's so, so
G F
sweet, gent - le words she soft - ly speaks. Such an an - gel when we
G F
need, God bless the ground be - neath her feet. She can take you on a
G Am
high, be your com - fort when you cry. But if you look in - to her
F G C F
eyes, you'll see the strength of a wo - man,__
G F C F G F
the strength of a wo - man.__ She'll put a
D.S. (fade out)

SULTANS OF SWING

♩ 148 | 8 Beat

1\.
Dm C B♭ A7
You get a shiver in the dark, it's raining in the park but meantime
Dm C B♭ A7
south of the river you stop and you hold everything.
F C
A band is blowing Dixie double four time.
B♭ Dm B♭ C
You feel alright, when you hear the music ring.

2\.
Dm C B♭ A7
Well now you step inside but you don't see too many faces
Dm C B♭ A7
comin' in out of the rain to hear the jazz go down.
F C
Competition in other places,
B♭ Dm B♭ C
ah, but the horns they're blowin' that sound
B♭ C
Way on down south,
Dm B♭ C Dm B♭ C
way on down south London town.

3\.
Dm C B♭ A7
You check out Guitar George, he knows all the chords.
Dm C B♭ A7
Mind his strictly rhythm, he doesn't want to make it cry or sing.
F C
He said an old guitar is all he can afford,
B♭ Dm B♭ C
when he gets up under the lights to play his thing.

4\.
Dm C B♭ A7
And Harry doesn't mind if he doesn't make the scene.
Dm C B♭ A7
He's got a day-time job, he's doin' alright.
F C
He can play the Honky-Tonk like anything,
B♭ Dm
saving it up for Friday night,
B♭ C B♭ C Dm B♭ C Dm B♭ C
with the Sultans, with the Sultans of Swing.

5\.
Dm C B♭ A7
And a crowd of young boys, they're foolin' around in the corner,
Dm C B♭ A7
drunk and dressed in their best brown baggies and their platform soles.
F C
They don't give a damn about any trumpet playin' band,
B♭ Dm
it ain't what they call Rock'n Roll.
B♭ C B♭ C Dm
And the Sultans, yeah, the Sultans play Creole.
B♭ C Dm B♭ C
Creole baby!

Dm C B♭ A7 Dm C B♭ A7 F C B♭ Dm B♭ C B♭ C Dm B♭ C Dm B♭ C
6. *Instrumental*

Dm C B♭ A7
7. And then The Man, he steps right up to the microphone
Dm C B♭ A7
and says at last, just as the time-bell rings:
F C
"Good night, now it's time to go home!"
B♭ Dm
And he makes it fast with one more thing:
B♭ C B♭ C
We are the Sultans,
Dm B♭ C Dm B♭ C
we are the Sultans of Swing!"

//: Dm B♭ C Dm B♭ C ://
8. *Instrumental, fade out nach Belieben*

Words & Music by Mark Knopfler

Dm
2.Well now you step in - side but you
C B♭ A7 Dm
don't see too ma-ny fa - ces com-in' in out of the
C B♭ A7 F
rain to hear the jazz go down. Com-pe-
C B♭
ti-tion in oth-er pla - ces, ah, but the
Dm
horns they're blow-in' that sound
B♭ C
Way on down
B♭ C
south, way on down south
Dm B♭ C
Lon-don town.
Dm B♭
C
D.S. (fade out, beim letzten mal)
3.You check out

SUMMER OF '69

♩	138	Rock

```
                 D
1.      I got my first real six-string,
        A
           bought it at the five and dime.
        D
           Played it 'till my fingers bled;
        A
           was the summer of sixty-nine.
        D
           Me and some guys from school
        A
           had a band and we tried real hard.
        D
           Jimmy quit and Jody got married,
        A
           I should'a known we'd never get far.
        Bm            A            D                        G      A
             Oh, when I look back now,   that summer seemed to last forever.
        Bm         A            D                    G         A
             And if I had the choice,   yeah, I'd always wanna be there.
        Bm                     A          D    A
             Those were the best days of my life.

        D
2.         Ain't no use in complainin'
        A
           when you got a job to do.
        D
           Spent my evenin's down at the drive-in,
        A
           and that's when I met you, yeah!
        Bm                     A          D                       G      A
             Standin' on your mama's porch,   you told me that you'd wait forever.
        Bm                      A          D                      G      A
             Oh, and when you held my hand,   I knew that it was now or never.
        Bm                     A          D    A
             Those were the best days of my life.
                                   D        A
        Back in the summer of sixty-nine.

        F                  Bb
Br.        Man, we were killin' time,
                 C                      Bb                F
        we were young and restless, we needed to unwind.
                  Bb               C
        I guess nothin' can last forever, forever, no!

Zw.     //: D     A     ://

        D
3.         And now the times are changin',
        A
           look at everything that's come and gone.
        D
           Sometimes when I play that old six-string,
```

A
I think about you, wonder what went wrong.
Bm **A** **D** **G** **A**
Standin' on your mama's porch, you told me it would last forever.
Bm **A** **D** **G** **A**
Oh, and when you held my hand, I knew that it was now or never.
Bm **A** **D** **A**
Those were the best days of my life.
D
Back in the summer of sixty-nine.
A **D** **A**
It was the summer of sixty-nine. Oh, yeah!
D **A**
Me and my baby in sixty-nine. Oh! ---

Outro **//: D A ://** (fade out)

Words & Music by Bryan Adams & Jim Vallance

D A
Jim-my quit and Jo-dy got mar-ried, I should-'a known we'd
Bm A
ne-ver get far. Oh, when I look back now,
D G A Bm
that sum - mer seemed to last for-e-ver. And if I
A D G A
had the choice, yeah, I'd al-ways wan-na be there.
Bm A D
Those were the best days of my life.
1. A 2. A
D
Back in the sum-mer of six-ty-nine.
A F
Man, we were

B♭
C
kil - lin' time, we were young and rest - less, we
B♭
F
B♭
need - ed to un - wind. I guess no - thin' can last for - e -
C
D
- ver, for - e - ver, no!
A
D.S. al 𝄌 (ohne Wdhlg.)
𝄌 A
D
It was the sum - mer of six - ty - nine. Oh, yeah!
A
D
Me and my ba - by in six - ty - nine.
A
D
Oh!
A
fade out

SUNDAY BLOODY SUNDAY

♩.	110	Rock

```
        Am C F   Am C F Am   C          F    Am C    F
Intro                          Mmh! Oh,--- oh,------- oh.----

        Am              C                   F
1.          I can't believe the news today,
        Am            C                    F
            I can't close my eyes and make it go away.
        C              Dm                                C                    Dm
          How long, how long must we sing this song,    how long, how lo---ong?
               Am   C  F                       Am   C   F
        But tonight-- we can be as one, tonight!---

        Am              C                F
2.          Broken bottles under children's feet
        Am                   C                  F
            and bodies strewn across the    dead-end streets.
        Am                    C                  F
            But I won't heed the battle call,
        Am                  C                   F
            it puts my back up puts my back up against the wall.

        Am           C              F        Am         C              F
Ref.        Sunday, bloody Sunday!        Sunday, bloody Sunday!
        Eb        Bb             C                            Eb       Bb C
           Sunday, bloody Sunday! Sunday, bloody Sunday!

        Am              C                F
3.          And the battle's just begun.
        Am                        C               F
            There's many lost, but tell me   who has won?
        Am                        C               F
            The trenches dug within our hearts
        Am                          C                   F
            and mother's children, brothers, sisters torn apart.   Ref. ...

        C              Dm                                C                    Dm
Zw.       How long, how long must we sing this song,     how long, how lo---ong?
               Am   C  F                       Am   C   F
        But tonight-- we can be as one, tonight!---
          Am  C      F        Am     C  F            Am C F   Am C F
        Tonight!   Tonight! Tonight! Tonight!  //:                      :// (2x)

                     Am     C F                    Am     C  F
        Wipe your tears away!    Wipe your tears away!
                     Am     C F                    Am     C  F                   Am      C  F
        Wipe your tears away!    Wipe your tears away!    Wipe your tears away!

             Eb         Bb             C                             Eb        Bb C
Ref.    //:    Sunday, bloody Sunday! Sunday, bloody Sunday!                 ://
```

4.
Am C F
And it's true we are immune
Am C F
when fact is fiction and T.V. is reality.
Am C F
And today the millions cry,
Am C F
we eat and drink while tomorrow they die.
Am C F Am C F
The real battle just begun, to claim the victory Jesus won.

Ref.
Am C F Am C F Am
//: Sunday, bloody Sunday! Sunday, bloody Sunday! ://
(2x)

Words & Music by U2

Am C F

Am C F Am C
sim. Mmh! Oh,

F Am C F
oh, oh.

Am C F
1.I can't be - lieve the news to - day,

Am C F
I can't close my eyes and make it go a - way.

C Dm C
How long, how long must we sing this song, how long, how

Dm Am C
long? But to - night

F Am C F
we can be as one, to - night!
Am C F
2.Bro-ken bot - tles un - der child-ren's feet
Am C F
and bo-dies strewn a-cross the dead-end streets.
Am C F Am C
But I won't heed the bat-tle call, it puts my back up puts my
F Am C
back up a-gainst the wall. Sun-day, bloo-dy Sun -
F Am C F
- day! Sun-day, bloo - dy Sun - day!
E♭ B♭ C
Sun-day, bloo - dy Sun - day! Sun-day, bloo - dy Sun -
E♭ B♭ C C
- day!
D.S.al Φ1
How long,
Dm C Dm
how long must we sing this song, how long, how long?

Am C F
But to - night we can be as one, to -
Am C F Am C F Am C
night! To - night! To - night! To - night! To -
F Am C F Am C F Am C
night!
F Am C F Am C
Wipe your tears a - way!
F Am C F Am C
Wipe your tears a - way! Wipe your tears a - way!
F E♭ B♭ C
Sun - day, bloo - dy Sun - day! Sun - day, bloo - dy Sun -
E♭ B♭ C Am C
- day! D.S. al 2
(3.) The real bat - tle just be -
F Am C F
gun, to claim the vic - to - ry Je - sus won.
Am C F
Sun - day, bloo - dy Sun - day!
Am C F Am
2 x wdhl.
Sun - day, bloo - dy Sun - day!

TAKE A CHANCE ON ME

♩	106	16 Pop

Ref.1
C
If you change your mind I'm the first in line,
G
honey, I'm still free, take a chance on me.
If you need me, let me know, gonna be around,
C
if you got no place to go when you're feeling down,
if you're all alone when the pretty birds have flown,
G
honey, I'm still free, take a chance on me.
Gonna do my very best and it ain't no lie
C
if you put me to the test, if you let me try,
Dm G Dm G
take a chance on me, take a chance on me.

1.
Dm C
We can go dancing, we can go walking as long as we're together,
Dm C
listen to some music, maybe just talking, you'd get to know me better
Am
'cause you know I got so much that I wanna do.
F Am F G
When I dream I'm alone with you, it's magic!--
Am F
You want me to leave it there afraid of a love affair,
Dm G Dm G
but I think you know that I can't let go. ***Ref.1 ...***

2.
Dm C
Oh, you can take your time, baby, I'm in no hurry, I know I'm gonna get you.
Dm C
You don't wanna hurt me, baby, don't worry, I ain't gonna let you.
Am
Let me tell you now my love is strong enough
F Am F G
to last when things are rough, it's magic!--
Am F
You say that I waste my time, but I can't get you off my mind,
Dm G Dm G
no, I can't let go 'cause I love you so.

Ref.2
C
If you change your mind I'm the first in line,
G
honey, I'm still free, take a chance on me.
If you need me, let me know, gonna be around,
C
if you got no place to go when you're feeling down,
if you're all alone when the pretty birds have flown,
G
honey, I'm still free, take a chance on me.

Gonna do my very best, baby, can't you see,

C
gotta put me to the test, take a chance on me.

C
//: Ba ba ba ba ba, ba ba ba ba ba.

G
Honey, I'm still free, take a chance on me.

Gonna do my very best, baby, can't you see,

C
gotta put me to the test, take a chance on me. :// (fade out)

G
take a chance on me.
Gon-na do my ve-
-ry best and it ain't no lie
if you put me to
C
Dm
the test, if you let me try, take a chance on me,
G
Dm
G
take a chance on me.
Dm
1.We can go danc - ing, we can go walk - ing as
C
long as we're to - ge - ther,
Dm
lis-ten to some mu - sic, may-be just talk - ing, you'd
C
get to know me bet - ter 'cause you know I got
Am
F
so much that I wan-na do. When I dream I'm a-lone with you, it's

Am F G Am
ma - gic! You want me to leave it there
F Dm
a - fraid of a love af - fair, but I think you know
G Dm 1. G
that I can't let go. If you change your mind
2. G D.S.al Φ Φ C
If you change your mind chance on me.
C
Ba ba ba ba ba, ba ba ba ba ba.
Hon - ey, I'm still free, take a chance on me.
G
Gon - na do my ve - ry best, ba - by, can't you see,
got - ta put me to the test, take a
C fade out
chance on me. Ba ba ba ba ba,

TEACH YOUR CHILDREN

♩ 156 Country-Fox

1.
D G D A
You who are on the road must have a code that you can live by,
D G D A
and so become yourself because the past is just a good bye.

Ref.1
D G D A
Teach your children well, their father's hell did slowly go by,
D G D A
and feed them on your dreams the one they picks, the one you'll know by.
D G D
Don't you ever ask them why, if they told you, you will cry,
Bm G A7 D G D A A7
so just look at them and sigh----- and know they love you.

2.
D G D A
And you, of tender years, can't know the fears that your elders grew by.
D G
And so please help them with your youth,
D A
they seek the truth before they can die.

Ref.2
D G D A
Teach your parents well, their children's hell will slowly go by,
D G D A
and feed them on your dreams the one they picks, the one you'll know by.
D G D
Don't you ever ask them why, if they told you, you will cry,
Bm G A7 D G D A7 D D2 D
so just look at them and sigh----- and know they love you.

Words & Music by Graham Nash
Crosby, Stills, Nash & Young

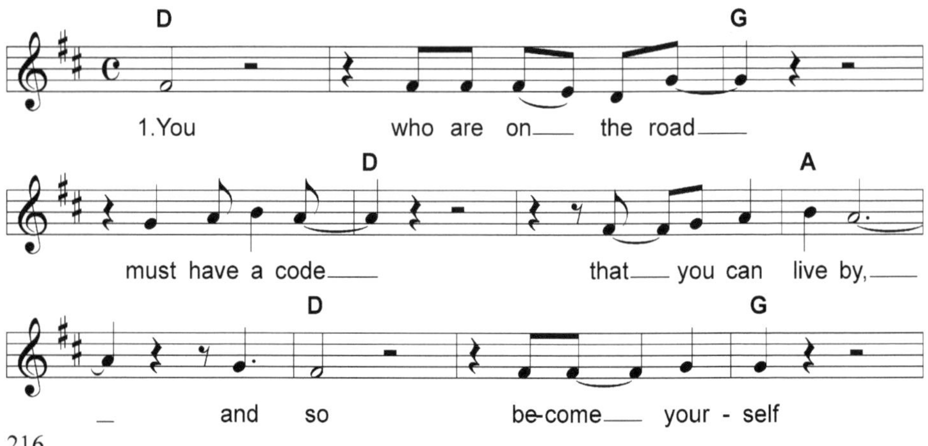

D
A
be-cause the past is just a good bye.
D
G
Teach your child - ren well,
D
A
their fa - ther's hell did slow - ly go by,
D
G
and feed them on your dreams
D
A
the one they picks, the one you'll know by.
D
G
Don't you e - ver ask them why, if they
D
told you, you will cry, so just look at them and
Bm
G
A7
D
sigh and know they love you.
G
D
A
A7
D.C.al Coda
2.And
D
G
D
A7
D
Dsus2
D
love you.

TEARS IN HEAVEN

♩	78	Ballad

```
        A                E         F#m  A D    A                E   E7
1.         Would you know my name,          if I saw you in heaven?
        A            E        F#m  A D      A               E    E7
           Would it be the same,         if I saw you in heaven?
        F#m                C#   E0              F#7
              I must be strong       and carry on,
              Bm               E4                  A   E F#m A D E4 E7 A
        cause I know I don't belong here in heaven.

        A                E         F#m  A D    A                E   E7
2.         Would you hold my hand,          if I saw you in heaven?
        A                E          F#m  A D   A                E   E7
           Would you help me stand,         if I saw you in heaven?
        F#m                C#   E0                   F#7
              I'll find my way       through night and day,
              Bm                  E4                 A   E F#m A D E4 E7 A
        'Cause I know I just can't stay here in heaven.

        C              Bm        Am                D            G   D Em D G
Br.        Time can bring you down. Time can bend your knees.
        C               Bm        Am               D         G     D            E     E7
           Time can break your heart. Have you begging please,    begging please?

        A                E         F#m  A D    A                E   E7
3.      (instrumental)
        A                E         F#m  A D    A                E   E7

        F#m                  C#  E0                   F#7
              Beyond the door,       there's peace I'm sure
             Bm                   E4                  A   E F#m A D E4 E7 A
        and I know there'll be no more tears in heaven.
```

1. Would you know my name, ...

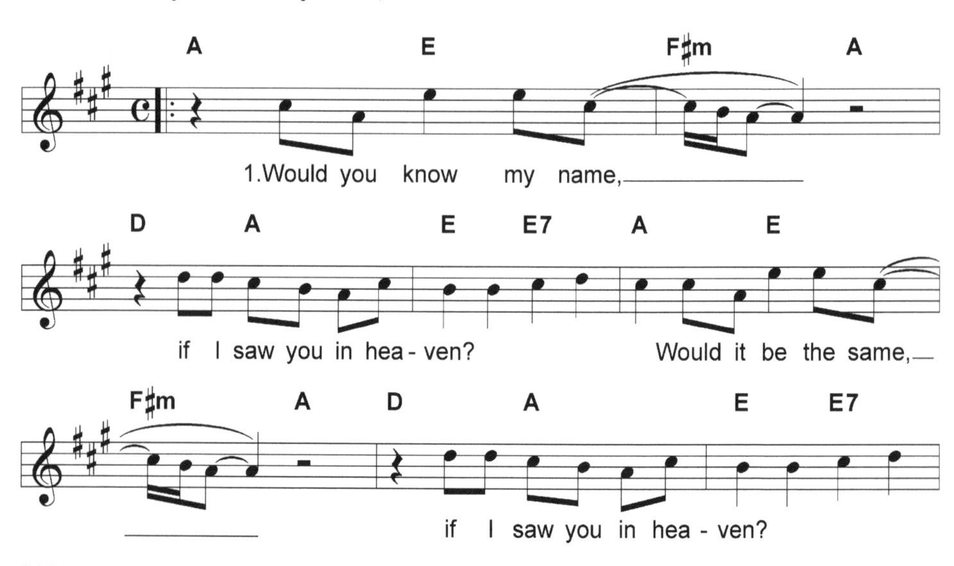

F♯m
C♯
E○
I must be strong
and car - ry on,
F♯7
Bm
Esus4
cause I know I don't be-long
here in hea-
A
E
F♯m
A
D
Esus4
E7
1.
A
ven.
2.
A
C
Bm
Time can bring you down.
Am
D
G
D
Time can bend your knees.
Em
D
G
C
Bm
Time can break your heart.
Am
D
G
D
Have you beg - ging please,
beg-ging please?
E
E7
A
E
D.C.al Coda (mit Wdhlg.)
ven.
F♯m
A
D
Esus4
E7
A
rit.

THE GREAT SONG OF INDIFFERENCE

𝅗𝅥	120	Blue Grass

```
        C               F          C                        G4
1.      I don't mind if you go, I don't mind if you take it slow.
        C                          F          C        G        C
        I don't mind if you say yes or no, I don't mind at all.
        C                      F          C                          G4
        I don't care if you live or die, couldn't care less if you laugh or cry.
        C                         F        C        G        C
        I don't mind if you crash or fly, I don't mind at all.
        C                         F          C                  G4
        I don't mind if you come or go, I don't mind if you say no.
          C                            F            C          G       C
        Couldn't care less baby let it flow, 'cos I don't care at all.

          C               F   C   G4   C   F   C G C
Ref.    Na na na, ...

Zw.     C   F   C   G4   C   F   C G C

        C                         F                C             G4
2.      I don't care if you sink or swim, lock me out or let me in.
            C                          F             C        G       C
        Where I'm going or where I've been, I don't mind at all.
        C                         F                 C                     G4
        I don't mind if the government falls, implements more futile laws.
        C                         F                 C        G       C
        I don't care if the nation stalls, and I don't care at all.
        C                         F                C                G4
        I don't care if they tear down trees, I don't feel the hotter breeze.
          C                    F            C        G       C
        Sink in dust in dying seas, and I don't care at all.

          C               F   C   G4   C   F   C G C
Ref.    Na na na, ...

Zw.     C   F   C   G4   C   F   C G C

        C                    F                  C                   G4
3.      I don't mind if culture crumbles, I don't mind if religion stumbles.
        C                        F                     C         G       C
        I can't hear the speakers mumble, and I don't mind at all.
        C                         F                      C                G4
        I don't care if the Third World fries, it's hotter there I'm not surprised.
              C                             F               C         G       C
        Baby I can watch whole nations die, and I don't care at all.
        C             F              C              G4
        I don't mind! I don't mind! I don't mind! I don't mind!
        C             F              C          G      C
        I don't mind! I don't mind! I don't mind at all!
```

Ref. **C** Na na na, ... **F C G4 C F C G C**

Zw. **C F C G4 C F C G C**

4. **C** I don't mind about people's fears, **F** authority **C** no longer **G4** hears.
C Send a social **F** engineer, and **C** I don't **G** mind at **C** all.

//: C F C G4 C F C G C ://
Instumental nach Belieben

And **C** I don't **G** mind at **C** all.

Words & Music by Bob Geldof

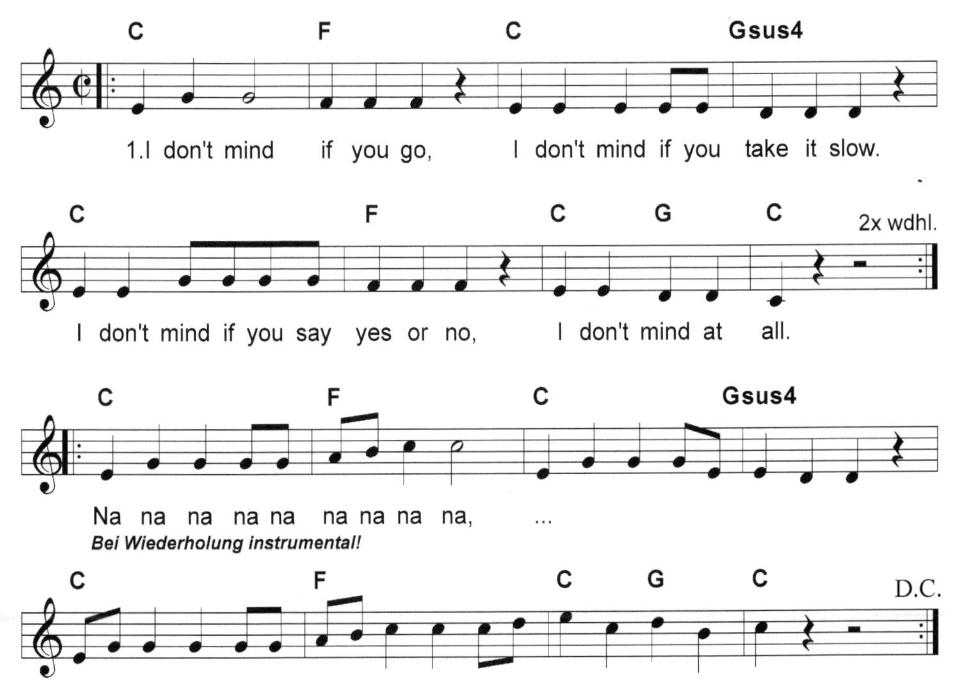

THE JOKER

𝅗𝅥	81	Reggae

1.
F B♭ C B♭
Some people call me the space cowboy,
F B♭ C B♭
some call me the gangster of love.
F B♭ C B♭
Some people call me Maurice,
F B♭ C B♭
'cause I speak of the pompitous of love.

2.
F B♭ C B♭
People talk about me baby,
F B♭ C B♭
say I'm doing you wrong, doing you wrong.
F B♭ C B♭
But don't you worry baby, don't you worry,
F B♭ C B♭
'cause I'm right here, right here, right here at home.

Ref.1
F B♭ F B♭
'cause I'm a picker, I'm a grinner, I'm a lover and I'm a sinner,
F B♭ C B♭
playing my music in the sun. ----
F B♭ F B♭
I'm a joker, I'm a smoker, I'm a midnight toker,
F B♭ C B♭
I sure don't want to hurt no one. ----

Ref.2
F B♭ F B♭
'cause I'm a picker, I'm a grinner, ... I'm a midnight toker,
F B♭ C
I get my loving on the run. Ooh! Ooh!

3.
F B♭ C B♭
You're the cutest thing that I ever did see,
F B♭ C B♭
I really love your peaches want to shake your tree.
F B♭ C B♭
Lovy dubby, lovy dubby, lovy dubby all the time
F B♭ C B♭
Oohwe baby I'll sure show you a good time.

Ref. 'cause I'm a picker, ... *(fade out)*

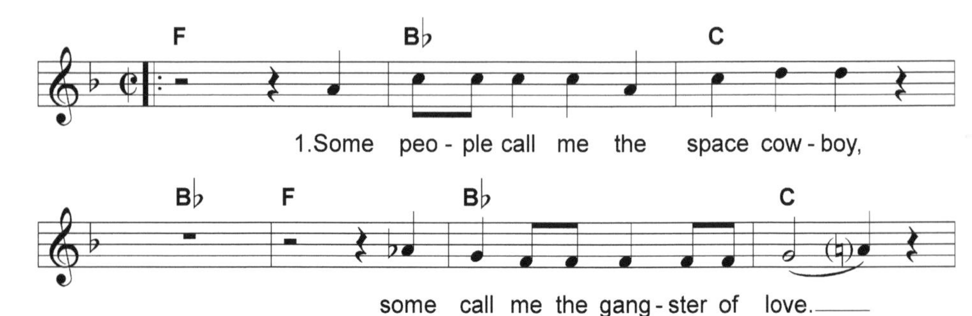

B♭ F B♭ C
Some peo-ple call me Mau-rice,
B♭ F B♭ 1. C
'cause I speak of the pom-pi-tous of love.
B♭ 2. C B♭ F
home. 'cause I'm a pick-er, I'm a
B♭ F B♭
grin-ner, I'm a lo-ver and I'm a sin-ner,
F B♭ C B♭
play-ing my mu-sic in the sun. I'm a
F B♭ F
jo-ker, I'm a smo-ker, I'm a mid-night to-
B♭ F B♭
-ker, I sure don't want to hurt no
1. C B♭ 2. C
one. I'm a run.
D.C.(ohne Wiederholung, fade out im Refrain)
Ooh! Ooh!

THE LADY IN RED

♩	76	16 Ballad

Intro: **G C D G C D**

1.
G C D
I've never seen you looking so lovely as you did tonight;
H7 Em D C
I've never seen you shine so bright. Mm mm mm.
G C D
I've never seen so many men ask you if you wanted to dance.
H7 Em G7 C
They're looking for a little romance, given half a chance.
Am
I have never seen that dress you're wearing,
D7 Em D
or the highlights in your hair that catch your eyes; I have been blind.

Ref.:
D7 G C D Em D Em
The lady in red is dancing with me cheek to cheek.
Am7 D7 G G7
There's nobody here, it's just you and me. It's where I wanna be.
C H7 Em A7
But I hardly know this beauty by my side.
Am7 D7 G C D G C D
I'll never forget the way you look tonight. *(Instrumental)*

2.
G C D
I've never seen you looking so gorgeous as you did tonight;
H7 Em D C
I've never seen you shine so bright. You were amazing.
G C D
I've never seen so many people want to be there by your side.
H7 Em G7 C
And when you turned to me and smiled it took my breath away.
Am
I have never had such a feeling.
D7 Em D
Such a feeling of complete and utter love as I do tonight.

Ref.:
D7 G D7 Em A7
The lady in red ... ... the way you look tonight.
Am7 D G
I'll never will forget the way you look tonight.

Words & Music by Chris de Burgh

G C D G C D
I've
G C
ne - ver seen you look - ing so love - ly as you did to - night;
D B7 Em D
I've ne - ver seen you shine so bright. Mm mm mm.
C G C
I've ne-ver seen so ma-ny men ask you if you want-ed to dance.
D B7 Em G7 3
They're look - ing for a lit - tle ro - mance, giv-en half a
C Am
chance. I have ne - ver seen that dress you're wear - ing, or the
D7
high - lights in your hair that catch your eyes;
Em D D7
I have been blind. The la - dy in red

G C D 3 Em D
_ is danc-ing with me cheek to cheek._
Em Am7
_ There's no - bo - dy here,_
D7 G
it's just you and me._ It's where I wan-na be.
G7 C B7
But I hard-ly know_ this beau-ty by my
Em A7 Am7
side._ I'll ne-ver for-get_
1.
D7 G
the way you look_ to-night._
2.
D7 Em A7
the way you look_ to-night._ I'll ne-ver will for-
Am7 D7 G
get the way you look to-night._

THE LOGICAL SONG

♩	122	8 Pop-Beat

1.
Am **F** **Em7**
When I was young, it seemed that life was so wonderful,
G **F** **F$^{\#o}$**
a miracle, oh it was beautiful, magical.
Am **F** **Em7**
And all the birds in the trees, well they'd be singing so happily,
G **F** **F$^{\#o}$**
oh, joyfully, oh, playfully, watching me.

2.
Am **F** **Em7**
But then they send me away to teach me how to be sensible,
G **F** **F$^{\#o}$**
logical, oh, responsible, practical.
Am **F** **Em7**
And they showed me a world where I could be so dependable,
G **F** **F$^{\#o}$**
oh, clinical, oh, intellectual, cynical.

Ref.
C **F$^{\#o}$7**
There are times when all the world's asleep,
Fj7 **B♭**
the questions run too deep for such a simple man.
C **F$^{\#o}$7**
Won't you please, please tell me what we've learned?
Fj7 **B♭**
I know it sounds absurd, please tell me who I am.

3.
Am **F** **Em7**
I said, now watch what you say or they'll be calling you a radical,
G **F** **F$^{\#o}$**
a liberal, oh, fanatical, criminal.
Am **F** **Em7**
Won't you sign up your name, we'd like to feel you're acceptable,
G **F** **F$^{\#o}$**
respecable, oh, presentable. A vegetable!

Solo **Am F Em7 G F F$^{\#o}$ Am F E7 G F F$^{\#o}$**

Ref.
C **F$^{\#o}$7** **B♭**
But at night, when all the world's asleep, ... who I am,
who I am, who I am, who I am.

Solo //: **A7** **Dm Am A7** **Dm Am F** :// *(fade out)*

Words & Music by Roger Hodgson & Richard Davies

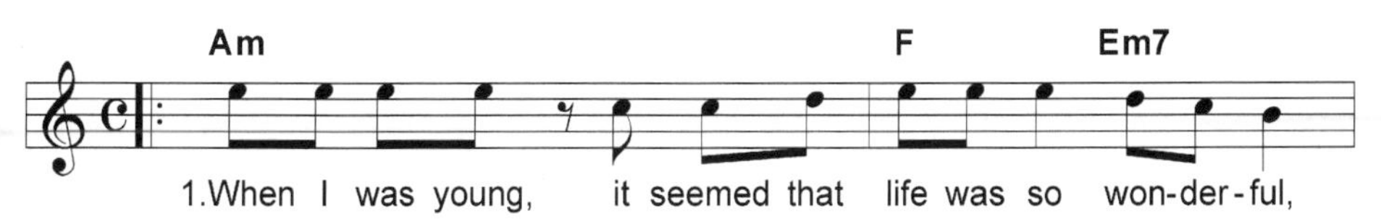

G F F♯°
a mir-a-cle, oh it was beau-ti-ful, mag-i-cal. And all the
Am F Em7
birds in the trees, well they'd be sing-ing so hap-pi-ly,
G F F♯°
oh, joy-ful-ly, oh, play-ful-ly, watch-ing me.
1. 2. C
2.But then they There are times when all
F♯°7
the world's a-sleep, the ques-
FMaj7
tions run too deep for such a sim-ple man.
B♭ C
Won't you please, please
F♯°7
tell me what we've learned? I know
FMaj7
it sounds ab-surd, please tell me who I am.
B♭ D.C.al Am
3.I said, now

F Em7 G F F♯° Am F Em7
G F F♯° C
But at night, when all the world's a - sleep,
F♯°7
the ques - tions run so deep
FMaj7
for such a sim - ple man.
B♭ C
Won't you please, please tell me what we've learned?
F♯°7
I know it sounds ab - surd,
FMaj7
please tell me who I am,
B♭
who I am, who I am, who I am.
A7
Dm Am A7 Dm Am F
fade out

TO BE WITH YOU

♩ 85 Rock

```
        C#m                  E    A                E
1.          Hold on, little girl, show me what he's done to you.
        C#m                   E    A                 E
            Stand up, little girl, broken heart can't be that bad,
           A           E              A                  E
        when it's through it's through. Fate with twist, the both of you,
          D                              B7
        so come on, Baby, come on over, let me be the one to show you.

        E                A        B7      E
Ref.    I'm the one who wants to be with you,
                      A        B7    E
        deep inside I hope you feel it, too.
                     A       B7          E
        Waited on a line of greens and blues
                      A          B7  E
        just to be the next to be with you.

        C#m                           E    A                E
2.          Build up your confidence, so you can be on top for once.
        C#m                             E  A               E
            Wake up who cares about little boys that talk too much.
          A    E              A                    E
        I seen it all to go down, your game of love was all rained out.
          D                              B7
        So come on, baby, come on over, let me be the one to hold you.

Ref.    I'm the one who...

        E4                               C#m
Zw.         Why be alone when we can be together, baby?
        G
        You can make my life worth while I can make you start to smile.

Gitarrensolo     E  A  B7  E    A  B7  E    A  B7  C#m  E  A  B7  E

           A           E              A                  E
        When it's through it's through. Fate with twist, the both of you,
          D                              B7
        so come on, baby, come on over, let me be the one to show you.

Ref.    I'm the one who...            (2x)
```

Musik und Text: ERIC LEE MARTIN,
DAVID RICHARD GRAHAME

C♯m
E
A
1.Hold on, lit - tle girl, show me what he's
E
C♯m
E
done to you. Stand up, lit - tle girl,
A
E
A
bro-ken heart can't be that bad, when it's through it's
E
A
E
through. Fate with twist, the both of you, so
D
come on, ba - by, come on ov - er,
B7
E
let me be the one to show you. I'm the one who
A
B7
E
wants to be with you, deep in - side I
A
B7
E
A
hope you feel it, too. Wait-ed on a line of
B7
E
A
greens and blues just to be the next to

B7 E Esus4
be with you.
Why be a-lone when we can
C♯m G
be to-geth - er, ba - by?
You can make my life
worth while
I can make you start to smile.
E A B7 E A B7 E
Gitarrensolo
A B7 C♯m E A B7
E A E
When it's through it's through.
A E
Fate with twist, the both of you, so
D
come on, ba - by, come on ov - er,
B7
let me be the one to show you.

G C D G
I'm the one who wants to be with you,
C D G
deep in - side I hope you feel it, too.
C D
Wait - ed on a line of greens and blues
G C D G
just to be the next to be with you.
E A B7 E
I'm the one who wants to be with you,
A B7 E
deep in - side I hope you feel it, too.
E A B7 C♯m
Wait-ed on a line of greens and blues
E A B7 E
just to be the next to be with you.

TORN

♩	97	16 Pop

```
        F                                  Am
1.        I thought I saw a man brought to life.
                                                 B♭7
        He was warm, he came around like he was dignified.

        He showed me what it was to cry.
        F                                   Am
          Well you couldn't be that man I adored.
                                                           B♭7
        You don't seem to know, don't seem to care what your heart is for.

        But I don't know him anymore.
               Dm                           C
        There's nothing where he used to lie  my conversation has run dry.
        Am                        C                  F
            That's what's going on,   nothing's fine I'm torn.

                    C                  Dm
Ref.    I'm all out of faith, this is how I feel.
                          B♭                        F
        I'm cold and I am shamed lying naked on the floor.
                        C                     Dm
        Illusion never changed into something real.
                         B♭                          F
        I'm wide awake and I can see the perfect sky is torn.
                    C               Dm  B♭
        You're a little late, I'm already torn.

        F                                     Am
2.         So I guess the fortune teller's right.
                                                         B♭7
        Should have seen just what was there and not some holy light.

        To crawl beneath my veins and now
        Dm                        C
        I don't care, I have no luck,   I don't miss it all that much.
        Am                         C                        F
             There's just so many things that I can't touch, I'm torn.


Ref.    I'm all out of faith, ...

         Dm   C B♭ Dm         F    C
        Torn!       Uuh! Uuh! Uuh! ---

               Dm                              C
3.      There's nothing where he used to lie, my inspiration has run dry.
        Am                         C                  F
            That's what's going on,   nothing's right, I'm torn.

                    C                  Dm
Ref.    I'm all out of faith, this is how I feel.
                          B♭                        F
        I'm cold and I am shamed lying naked on the floor.
                        C                     Dm
        Illusion never changed into something real.
```

B♭ F
I'm wide awake and I can see the perfect sky is torn.
C Dm
I'm all out of faith, this is how I feel.
B♭ F
I'm cold and I'm ashamed bound and broken on the floor.
C Dm C B♭ Dm C
You're a little late, I'm already torn. Torn!

//: F C Dm B♭ ://
Zw. *Instrumental / fade out*

F
1.I thought I saw a man brought to life.

Am
He was warm, he came a-round like he was

B♭7
dig-ni-fied. He showed me what it was to cry.

F
Well you could-n't be that man I a-dored.

Am
You don't seem to know, don't seem to care what your

B♭7
heart is for. But I don't know him a-ny-more. There's

Dm C
noth-ing where he used to lie my con-ver-sa-tion has run dry.

Am
C
That's what's go-ing on, nothing's fine I'm
F
C
torn. I'm all out of faith, this is how I
Dm
B♭
feel. I'm cold and I am shamed ly-ing na-ked on the
F
C
floor. Il-lu-sion ne-ver changed in-to some-thing
Dm
B♭
real. I'm wide a-wake and I can see the per-fect sky is
F
C
Dm
B♭
torn. You're a lit-tle late, I'm al-rea-dy torn.
Dm
C
B♭
Dm
F
Torn! Uuh! Uuh! Uuh!
C
Dm
3.There's noth-ing where he used to lie. My
C
Am
in-spi-ra-tion has run dry. That's what's go-ing on,

Words & Music by Anne Previn, Scott Cutler & Phil Thornalley

TUBTHUMPING

♩	105	Pop-Rap

```
     D         G        D              G       D         G         D A
       We'll be singing,   when we're winning.   We'll be singing.

                     D               G
Ref.  I get knocked down, but I get up again.
            D                        G
      You're never gonna keep me down.
            D                        G
      I get knocked down, but I get up again.
             A
      You're never gonna keep me down.
                     D               G
      I get knocked down, but I get up again.
            D                        G
      You're never gonna keep me down.
            D                        G
      I get knocked down, but I get up again.
             A
      You're never gonna keep me down.

      Em G              Bm      A  Em G              Bm      A
Zw.          Pissing the night away.       Pissing the night away.

                      D                           G
Rap   He drinks a whisky drink, he drinks a vodka drink,
                    D                        G
      he drinks a lager drink, he drinks a cider drink.
                      D                              G
      He sings the songs that remind him of the good times,
                      A
      he sings the songs that remind him of the better times.

      D    G     D    G     D    G      A
Zw.   Oh, Danny Boy, Danny Boy, Danny Boy!

Ref.  I get knocked down, ...

Zw.   Pissing the night away. Pissing the night away.

Rap   He drinks a whisky drink, ...

        D    G    D  G         D       G  A
Zw.   Don't cry for me, next door neighbour!---

Ref.  I get knocked down, ...        (3x, beim 3.mal fade out)
```

Word & Music by Alice Nutter, Louise Watts, Judith Abbott, Nigel Hunter, Darren Hamer, Allan Whalley, Paul Greco, Duncan Bruce

D G D G D
We'll be sing-ing, when we're win-ning.
G D A
We'll be sing-ing. I get knocked
D G
down, but I get up a-gain. You're ne-
D G
-ver gon-na keep me down. I get knocked
D G
down, but I get up a-gain. You're ne-
A
-ver gon-na keep me down. I get knocked
D G
down, but I get up a-gain. You're ne-
D G
-ver gon-na keep me down. I get knocked
D G
down, but I get up a-gain. You're ne-

A Em G
- ver gon-na keep me down. Pis-sing the night
Bm A Em G Bm A
a-way. Pis-sing the night a-way. He drinks a
D G
whis-ky drink, he drinks a vod-ka drink, he drinks a
D G
la-ger drink, he drinks a ci-der drink. He sings the
D G
songs that re-mind him of the good times, he sings the
A D G
songs that re-mind him of the bet-ter times. Oh, Dan-ny Boy,
D G D G A
D.S.al Coda
Dan-ny Boy, Dan-ny Boy! I get knocked
D G D G
Don't cry for me, next door
D G A
D.S.and fade out (im Refrain)
neigh-bour! I get knocked

VERTIGO

♩ 140 | Rock

E5 A5
1. Lights go down, it's dark.
E5 A5
The jungle is your head, can't rule your heart.
E5 A5
I'm feeling so much stronger than before. Your eyes are wide.
E5 A5
And though your soul it can't be bought, your mind can wonder.

E D G A
Ref. Hello, hello! I'm at a place called Vertigo.
E D
It's everything I wish I didn't know.
G A E5 A5 E5 A5
Except you give me something. I can feel, feel.

E5 A5
2. The night is full of holes.
E5 A5
There's bullets ripping sky of ink with gold.
E5 A5
They twinkle as the boys play rock and roll.
E5 A5
They know that they can't dance, at least they know.

E5 A5
Br. I can't stand the beat. I'm asking for the cheque.
E5 A5
Girl with crimson nails. It's Jesus 'round her neck.
E5 A5
Swinging to the music. Swinging to the music.
E5 A5 E
Wow!----- Wow!----- Wow!----- ***Ref. ...***

A G A G A G A
Zw. Check mated? Just for jumping in. Yeah!

//: E A E A ://

Em
All of this, all of this can be yours.
E4
All of this, all of this can be yours.
Em
All of this, all of this can be yours.
E4 Em
Just give me what I want and no one gets hurt.

E D G A
Ref. Hello, hello! Might I please go Vertigo.
E D G A
Lights go down and no one knows that you give me something.
E D G A
I can feel your love teaching me how. ----
E D G A E5 A5 E5 A5
Your love is teaching me how, ------ how to kneel, kneel.

E5 A5 E5
Yeah, yeah, yeah, yeah, yeah, yeah, yeah, yeah!
A5 E5
Yeah, yeah, yeah, yeah, yeah, yeah, yeah, yeah!

A
E5
A5
E5
- thing. I can feel, feel.
A5
E5
2.The night is full of
A5
E5
holes. There's bul - lets rip - ping sky of ink with
A5
E5
gold. They twin - kle as the boys play rock and
A5
E5
roll. They know that they can't dance, at least they
A5
E5
know. I can't stand the beat. I'm ask - ing for the
A5
E5
cheque. Girl with crim - son nails. It's Je - sus 'round her
A5
E5
neck. Swing - ing to the mu - sic. Swing - ing to the
A5
E5
mu - sic. Wow! Wow!

A5 E D
_ Wow! Hel - lo, hel - lo!
G A E
Might I please go Ver - ti - go. It's eve - ry - thing I wish I
D G
did - n't know. Ex - cept you give me some -
A E5 A5 E5
- thing. I can feel, feel.
A5 A G A G A
Check ma - ted? Just for
G A E
jump - ing in. Yeah!
A E
A Em
All of this, all of this can be yours.
Esus4 Em
All of this, all of this can be yours. All of this,

Esus4
all of this can be yours. Just give me what I want and
Em E D
no one gets hurt. Hel-lo, hel-lo!
G A E
Might I please go Ver - ti - go. Lights go down and
D G
no one knows that you give me some -
A E D
- thing. I can feel your love teach - ing me how.
G A E D
Your love is teach - ing me how,
G A E5 A5 E5
how to kneel, kneel.
A5 E5 A5
Yeah, yeah, yeah, yeah, yeah, yeah, yeah,
E5 A5 E5
yeah! Yeah, yeah, yeah, yeah, yeah, yeah, yeah, yeah!

VENUS

♩	128	8 Beat

Em A Em A Em A Em A
1. Goddess on the mountain top, burning like a silver flame,
Em A Em A Em A Em
the summit of beauty and love, and Venus was her name.

Am D Am D Em A Em A
Ref. She's got it, yeah, baby, she's got it!
C B7 Em A Em A
Well, I'm your Venus, I'm your fire, at your desire.
C B7 Em A Em A
Well, I'm your Venus, I'm your fire, at your desire.

Em A Em A Em A Em A
2. Her weapons were her crystal eyes, making every man a man,
Em A Em A Em A Em
black as the dark night she was, got what no one else had. Wow!

Ref. She's got it, ... **// B**

Em A Em A Em A Em A Em A Em A Em A Em
Zw. Ah!... Ah!...

Ref. She's got it, ...

1. *instrumental und fade out*

Words & Music by Robert van Leeuwen

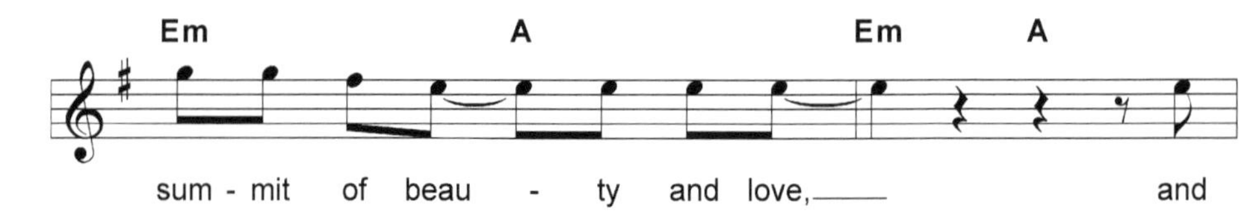

Em A Em Am D
Ve-nus was her name. She's got it,
Am D Em A Em A
yeah, ba - by, she's got it! Well,
C B7 Em A
I'm your Ve-nus, I'm your fi - re, at your de - si re.
Em A C B7
Well, I'm your Ve-nus, I'm your fi - re, at your
Em A 1. Em A 2. Em A B
de - si - re. 2.Her
Em A Em A Em A Em A
Ah!...
Em A Em A Em A Em
Ah!... She's
D.S. (dann Vers instrumental und fade out)

WE ARE THE CHAMPIONS

♩. 63 | Slow Rock

Am Em7 Am Em7
1. I've paid my dues, time after time,
Am Em7 Am Em7
I've done my sentence but committed no crime.
C F C F
And bad mistakes, I've made a few.
C G Am D7 G
I've had my share of sand kicked in my face, but I've come through,
A
and I need to go on, and on, and on, and on.

D F#m Bm G A
Ref. We are the champions my friend,
D F#m G D#°7
and we'll keep on fighting till the end.
Em A Gm
We are the champions, we are the champions,
D D7 F G7 A4
no time for losers, 'cause we are the champions
Dm (G Dm G Dm A4)
of the world.

Am Em7 Am Em7
2. I've taken my bows and my curtain calls.
Am Em7
You brought me fame and fortune and everything that goes with it,
Am Em7 C F C F
I thank you all. But it's been no bed of roses, no pleasure cruise.
C G Am D7 G
I consider it a challenge before the whole human race and I ain't gonna lose,
A
and I need to go on, and on, and on, and on.

Ref. We are the champions my friend, ...

Em7 C F C F
And bad mis - takes, I've made a few. I've had my
C G Am D7
share of sand kicked in my face, but I've come
G A
through, and I need to go on, and on, and on, and on.
D F♯m Bm G A
We are the cham - pions my friend, and
D F♯m G D♯°7
we'll keep on fight - ing till the end.
Em A Gm D
We are the cham - pions, we are the cham - pions, no time for
D7 F G7 Asus4
lo - sers, 'cause we are the cham - pions of the
Dm G Dm
world.
G Dm Asus4 D.S.
2.I've tak - en my

WE CAN WORK IT OUT

♩ 105 | 16 Beat

```
       G                                                          F         G
1.        Try to see it my way, do I have to keep on talking till I can't go on?
       While you see it your way,
                                           F                  G
       run the risk of knowing that our love may soon be gone.
         C              G     C              D
       We can work it out. We can work it out.

       G
2.        Think of what you're saying,
                                             F                 G
       you can get it wrong and still you think that it's all right.
       Think of what I'm saying,
                                         F                    G
       we can work it out and get it straight, or say goodnight.
         C              G     C              D
       We can work it out. We can work it out.

        Em                          Em7      C6      B7
Zw.:   Life is very short, and there's no time -----
                           Em              Em7   CMaj7  Em
       for fussing and fighting my friend.
                                       Em7   C6      B7
       I have always thought that it's a crime, ----
                  Em       Em7    CMaj7  Em
       so I will ask you once again.

       G                                                      F            G
3.        Try to see it my way, only time will tell if I am right or I am wrong.
       While you see it your way.
                                               F              G
       There's a chance that we might fall apart before too long.
         C              G     C              D
       We can work it out. We can work it out.

Zw.:   Life is very short, and there's no time ...

3.     Try to see it my way, ...

        C                G     C              D      G   G2  G
       We can work it out. We can work it out.
```

Words & Music by John Lennon & Paul McCartney

G
Try to see it my way, do I have to keep on talk-ing
F G
till I can't go on? While you see it your way,
F G
run the risk of know - ing that our love may soon be gone.
C G C D
We can work it out. We can work it out.
Em Em7 C6
Life is ve-ry short, and there's no time
B7 3 Em 3 Em7 CMaj7 Em
for fuss-ing and fight-ing my friend.
Em7 C6
I have al-ways thought that it's a crime,
B7 Em 3 Em7 3 CMaj7 Em
so I will ask you once a - gain.
2x D.C. (2.mal al Coda)
C G C D
We can work it out. We can work it out.
G 3 Gsus2 3 G

WHEN I'M SIXTY FOUR

♩	140	Foxtrot

C G
1. When I get older losing my hair, many years from now,
G7 C
will you still be sending me a valentine, birthday greetings, bottle of wine?
C7 F
If I'd been out till quarter to three would you lock the door?
Fm C A7 D7 G7 C
Will you still need me, will you still feed me, when I'm sixty-four?

Am G Am E7
Zw. You'll be older, too.
Am Dm Em F G7 C G G7
And if you say the word, I could stay with you.

C G
2. I could be handy, mending a fuse, when your lights have gone.
G7 C
You can knit a sweater by the fireside, sunday morning go for a ride.
C7 F
Doing the garden, digging the weeds, who could ask for more?
Fm C A7 D7 G7 C
Will you still need me, will you still feed me, when I'm sixty-four?

Am G
Zw. Every summer we can rent a cottage in the Ilse of Wight,
Am E7
if it's not too dear.We shall scrimp and save.
Am Dm Em F G7 C G G7
Grandchildren on your knee, Vera, Chuck and Dave.

C G
3. Send me a postcard, drop me a line, stating point of view.
G7 C
Indicate precisely what you mean to say, yours sincerely, wasting away.
C7 F
Give me your answer, fill in a form mine for evermore.
Fm C A7 D7 G7 C
Will you still need me, will you still feed me, when I'm sixty-four?

Words & Music by John Lennon & Paul McCartney Beatles

G7
C
val - en - tine,
birth-day gree-tings,
bot - tle of wine?
If
I'd been
out
till
quar - ter to three
C7
F
would
you
lock
the
door?
Fm
C
A7
Will you still need me,
will you still feed me,
D7
G7
C
Fine
Am
when I'm six - ty - four?
G
Am
You'll be
E7
Am
old - er, too.
And if you
Dm
Em
F
G7
say the word,
I could stay with
2x D.C.
2.mal al Fine
C
G
G7
you.

WE HAVE A DREAM

♩	68	16 Ballad

G D Em
1. We believe the dream comes true,
Bm C G Am D
everything that tried to do it wasn't easy all the time.
G D Em
We never felt like this before,
Bm C G Am D
but we love it more and more every day and every night.
Am D Bm Em
We enjoy and we have pain, come and let us start again.
Am C D
Music is what we're living for.

G Am
Ref. We have a dream, music is our life,
D C G D
we have a hope, music will survive.
G G7 C
We'll take a chance we had it all,
G D
we feel like heroes, we're standing tall.

G D Em
2. We all have the greatest time,
Bm C G Am D
hearts were beating with their blind, may I dream my dream with you.
G D Em
Oh I, I was sometimes so alone,
Bm C G Am D
couldn't make it on my own but my friends they're helping me.
Am D Bm Em
We cried tears, we have fun and we're singing our song.
Am C D
Music is what we're living for.

Ref. We have a dream, ...

G G D
Ref. We have a dream, ... we feel like heroes, we're standing tall,

standing tall, standing tall!

G D G Em
Ref. We have a dream, ... we're standing tall,

G C E♭ F G
We have a hope!--- We have a dream!

Words & Music by Dieter Bohlen

G D Em Bm
1.We be-lieve the dream comes true, eve-ry-thing that tried to
C G Am D
do it was-n't ea - sy all the time.
G D Em Bm
We nev-er felt like this be - fore, but we love it more and
C G Am D
more eve-ry day and eve - ry night.
Am D Bm Em
We en-joy and we have pain, come and let us start a-gain.
Am C D
Mu - sic is what we're liv-ing for. We have a
G Am D C
dream, mu-sic is our life, we have a hope, mu-sic will sur-
G D G G7
vive. We'll take a chance we had it

C G 1. D
all, we feel like he-roes, we're stand-ing tall.
2. D G
tall. We have a dream,
Am D
mu-sic is our life, we have a hope, mu-sic will sur-
G D G C
vive. We'll take a chance we had it all, we feel like
G D
he-roes, we're stand-ing tall, stand-ing tall, stand-ing tall!
D.S.al Coda
D G
We have a tall.
Em G C E♭ F G
We have a hope! We have a dream!
rit.

WHEN THE RAIN BEGINS TO FALL

♩	153	Eurobeat Disco

1.
Am   Amj7   Am7   Dm
Like the sand can seep right through your fingers,
E7   Am   Amj7   Am7
so can all your days as those days go by,
        Dm   G   Cm
you'll have me there to help you find the way.
  Cmj7   Cm7   Dm   G
I feel with you, I know it's got to last forever.

Ref.
Am   Dm   G   E7   Am
     And when the rain begins to fall, you are my rainbow in the sky.
              Dm   G   E7   Am
And I will catch you if you fall, you'll never have to ask me why.
                 Dm   G   E7   Am
And when the rain begins to fall, I'll be the sunshine in your life.
                  Dm   G   E7   Am
You know that we can have it all and everything will be allright.

2.
Am   Amj7 Am7   Dm   E7   Am
Time goes by so fast you've got to have a dream to just hold on.
          Amj7   Am7   Dm   G   Cm
All my dreams of love began with the reality of you
    Cmj7Cm7   Dm   G
and I believe that all the dreams will last forever.

Ref. And when the rain begins to fall, ...

Br.
   Dm   G   E7   Am   Dm
Though the sun may hide   we still can see the light,
        G   E7 Am
that shines for you and me.
        F   G   Am   Dm7 G
We'll be together all that we can be.

Ref. And when the rain begins to fall, ... *(2x, fade out)*

Words & Music by Peggy March, Mike Bradley, Steve Wittmack

Am Am/maj7 Am7 Dm
1.Like the sand can seep right through your fin - gers,
E7 Am Am
so can all your days as those
Am/maj7 Am7 Dm G
days go by, you'll have me there to help you find the
Cm Cm/maj7 Cm7 Dm
way. I feel with you, I know it's got to last
G Am Dm
for - e - ver. And when the rain be-gins to fall,
G E7 Am
you are my rain - bow in the sky. And I will
Dm G E7
catch you if you fall, you'll ne - ver have to ask me why.
Am Dm G
And when the rain be-gins to fall, I'll be the

E7 Am Dm
sun-shine in your life. You know that we can have it all
G E7 Am
and eve-ry-thing will be all-right.
1.
2.
Dm
Though the
G E7 Am
sun may hide we still can see the
Dm G E7 Am
light, that shines for you and me. We'll
F G Am Dm7 G
be to-ge-ther all that we can be.
D.S. and fade out

WHO'LL STOP THE RAIN

♩	123	8 Beat

Intro **G D Em D G**

```
    G                          C                 G
1.  Long as I remember the rain been comin' down.
                         Bm          C                G
    Clouds of myst'ry pourin' confusion on the ground.
     C                       G     C                G
    Good men through the ages tryin' to find the sun;
    C                D               Em          G
    and I wonder, still I wonder, who'll stop the rain.
```

```
    G                                  C                G
2.  I went down Virginia, seekin' shelter from the storm.
                        Bm       C                    G
    Caught up in the fable, I watched the tower grow.
     C                     G             C                    G
    Five-year plans and new deals wrapped in golden chains.
    C                D               Em          G
    And I wonder, still I wonder, who'll stop the rain.
```

Zw. **C G D Am C Em D G**

```
      G                             C                  G
3.  Heard the singers playing, how we cheered for more.
                               Bm       C              G
    The crowd had rushed together tryin' to keep warm.
     C                   G       C             G
    Still the rain kept pourin' falling on my ears.
    C                D               Em
    And I wonder, still I wonder, who'll stop the rain.
```

Outro **//: G D Em D ://** *(fade out)*

Words & Music by John C Fogerty

G D Em D G
G
1.Long as I re - mem - ber the
C G
rain been com - in' down. Clouds of mys - t'ry pour -
Bm C G
- in' con - fu - sion on the ground.
C G C
Good men through the a - ges try - in' to find the sun;
G C D
and I won - der, still I won - der,
Em G C G D
who'll stop the rain.
Am C Em D G
D.S.al Coda
Em
who'll stop the rain.
G D Em D fade out

WILD THING

♩ 101 | Rock-Beat

```
Intro:  G C D

        G            C D C                G           C D C
Ref.:   Wild thing,           you make my heart sing,
                    G       C         D   C     G         C D F G F G
        you make everything groovy,       wild thing!

        (G)                                 F G F G
1.          Wild thing, I think I love you,
                                      F G F G
        but I wanna' know for sure.
                                     F G F G
        Come on and hold me tight,
                     // G C D C G C D C
        I love you.

        G            C D C                G           C D C
Ref.:   Wild thing,           you make my heart sing,
                    G       C         D   C     G         C D
        you make everything groovy,       wild thing!

Zw.:    G C D C G C D C G C D C G C D  F G F G

        (G)                                 F G F G
2.      Wild thing, I think you move me,
                                      F G F G
        but I wanna' know for sure.
                                     F G F G
        Come on and hold me tight,
                         // G C D C G C D
        you move me.

            G            C D C                G           C D C
Ref.:   //: Wild thing,           you make my heart sing,
                    G       C         D   C     G         C D C
        you make everything groovy,       wild thing!       Oh, come on! ://
                                                                 (fade out)
```

G C D G C
Wild thing,
D C G C D C
you make my heart sing, you make eve -
G C D C G C
- ry - thing groo - vy, wild thing!
D F G F G
1.Wild thing, I
F G F G
think I love you, but I wan - na' know
F G F G
for sure. Come on and
F G F G
hold me tight, I love you.
G C D C G C D C

G C D C G C
Wild thing, you make my heart sing,
D C G C D C
you make eve - ry-thing groo - vy,
G C D G C
wild thing!
D C G C D C
G C D C
3 3 3
G C D F G F G
2.Wild thing, I
F G F G
think you move me, But I wan-na' know
F G F G
for sure. Come on and

F G F G
hold me tight,
you move me.
G C D C G C
D
G C D C
Wild thing,
you make my
G C D C G C
heart sing,
you make eve - ry-thing groo - vy,
D C G C D C
fade out
wild thing!
Oh, come on!

WISH YOU WERE HERE

𝅗𝅥	60	Ballad

Intro **Em G Em G Em A7/4 Em A7/4 G**

1\.
C D Am G
So, so you think you can tell heaven from hell, blue skies from pain.
D C Am
Can you tell a green field from a cold steel rail, a smile from a veil?
G
Do you think you can tell?
C D Am
And did they get you to trade your heroes for ghosts, hot ashes for trees,
G D
hot air for a cool breeze, cold comfort for change?
C Am G
And did you exchange a walk on part in the war for a lead role in a cage?

Zw. **Em G Em G Em A7/4 Em A7/4 G**

2\.
C D
How I wish, how I wish you were here.
Am G
We're just two lost souls swimming in a fish bowl, year after year,
D C
running over the same old ground. What have we found?
Am G
The same old fears. Wish you were here.

Outro //: **Em G Em G Em A7/4 Em A7/4 G** ://
(fade out)

Words & Music by David Gilmour & Roger Waters

Em G

Em A7sus4 G

C D
1.So, so you think you can tell

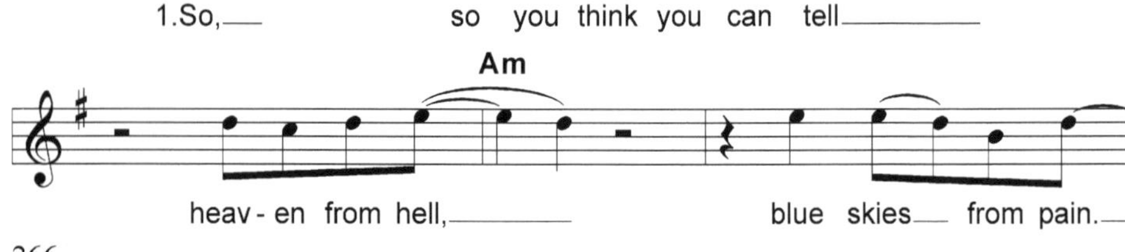

G D
Can you tell a green field
C
from a cold steel rail, a smile from a
Am G
veil? Do you think you can tell?
C
And did they get you to trade
D
your he - roes for ghosts, hot ash - es for trees,
Am G
hot air for a cool breeze,
D
cold com-fort for change? And did you ex -
C Am
change a walk on part in the war for a lead
G
role in a cage?
D.S.

WITHOUT YOU

𝅗𝅥	65	Ballad

```
           D                                      F#m
1.    No, I can't forget this evening or your face as you were leaving,
           Em                                        F#7
      but I guess that's just the way the story goes.
                       Bm                D                   E
      You always smile, but in your eyes your sorrow shows,
             D     A7
      yes it shows.

           D                                   F#m
2.    No, I can't forget tomorrow when I think of all my sorrow.
             Em                                      F#7
      When I had you there, but then I let you go.
                      Bm              D                E
      And now it's only fair that I should let you know
                              D     A7
      what you should know.

             D     Bm
Ref.  I can't live if living is without you.
            Em              A7
      I can't live, I can't give anymore.
            D      Bm
      I can't live if living is without you.
             Em             A7
      I can't give, I can't give any more.

1.    Well I can't forget this evening or your face ...

Ref.  I can't live ...      (fade out im Refrain)
```

D.S. (fade out im Refrain, ohne Wiederholung)

WONDERFUL TONIGHT

♩	95	16 Pop-Beat

```
        G                     D/F#       C                             D
1.         It's late in the evening,       she's wond'ring what clothes to wear.
        G                          D/F#     C                          D
           She puts on her makeup       and brushes her long blonde hair.
        C                  D          G              Bm/F#  Em
           And then she asks me:       "Do I look all right?"
                       C               D                G        (D/F#   C    D7)
        And I say: "Yes, you look wonderful tonight!"

        G                   D/F#   C                   D
2.          We go to a party,      and everyone turns to see
        G                       D/F#   C                 D
            this beautiful lady        is walking around with me.
        C                    D           G                Bm/F#  Em
            And then she asks me:    "Do you feel all right?"
                       C            D             G
        And I say: "Yes, I feel wonderful tonight!"

                   C                D                 G            Bm/F#   Em
Br.     I feel wonderful because I see the love light in your eyes.
                      C               D                    C                D
        And the wonder of it all is that you just don't realize
                        G              D/F#   C    D7    G    D/F#   C    D7
        how much I love you.

        G                           D/F#         C                           D
3.          It's time to go home now,      and I've got an aching head.
        G                              D/F#        C                         D
            So I gave her the car keys,      and she helps me to bed.
        C                   D         G             Bm/F#            Em
            And then I tell her,     as I turn out the light,
                         C                  D                 G        D/F#   Em  G/D
        I say: "My Darling, you are wonderful tonight!
                    C                       D                 G        D/F#  C  D7  G  D/F#  C  D7 G
        Oh, my Darling, you are wonderful tonight!"
```

Words & Music by Eric Clapton

G
D/F♯
1.It's late in the eve - ning,
C
D
she's won - d'ring what clothes to wear.
G
D/F♯
C
She puts on her make - up and brush - es her long
D
C
D
blonde hair. And then she asks me:
G
Bm/F♯
Em
C
"Do I look all right?" And I say: "Yes, you look
D
1.
G
D/F♯
won - der - ful to - night!"
C
D7
2.
G
night!" I feel
C
D
G
Bm/F♯
won - der - ful be - cause I see the love light in your

Em C D
eyes. And the won - der of it all is that you
C D G
just don't re - a - lize how much I love you.
D/F♯ C D7 G
D/F♯ C D7 D.C.al ⊕
⊕ G D/F♯
night!"
Em G/D C D
3
Oh, my Dar - ling, you are won - der - ful to -
G D/F♯ C D7
night!"
G D/F♯ C D7 G
rit.

YELLOW SUBMARINE

♩ 112 Shuffle

1.
D C G Em Am C D
In the town, where I was born, lived a man who sailed to sea,
G D C G Em Am C D
and he told us of his life in the land of submarines.

2.
G D C G Em Am C D
So we sailed up to the sun till we found the sea of green,
G D C G Em Am C D
and we lived beneath the waves in our yellow submarine.

Ref.
G D G
//: We all live in a yellow submarine, yellow submarine, yellow submarine. ://

3.
G D C G Em Am C D
And our friends are all aboard, many more of them live next door,
G D C G D G
and the band begins to play. *Ref. We all live ...*

4.
G D C G Em Am C D
As we live a life of ease, everyone of us has all we need,
G D C G Em Am C D
sky of blue and sea of green in our yellow submarine. *Ref. We all live ... (fade out)*

YOU'VE GOT A FRIEND

♩	84	Ballad

```
                     Am         E7                     Am        E7    Am
1.     When you're down and troubled and you need some lovin' care
           Dm7       G                  C
       and nothing, nothing is going right.
         Bm7                  E7         Bm E7       Am E7          Am
       Close your eyes and think of me          and soon I will be there,
           Dm7        Em                   G2     G  G4
       to brighten up even your darkest nights.

         G        C                               F
Ref.   You just call out my name and you know wherever I am.
                C                          F2/G     G
       I come running to see you again.
         C                             Cj7   F                        Am  C7
       Winter, spring, summer or fall, all you have to do is call
                F          Em Dm7 F2/G                   C        (F     C  Bm7  E7)
       and I'll be there.-----------          You've got a friend.

                 Am  E7                Am       E7      Am
2.     If the sky above you grows dark and full of clouds
                  Dm7         G                 C
       and that old north wind begins to blow.
        Bm7                   E7      Bm E7       Am             E7         Am
       Keep your head together              and       call my name out loud.
         Dm7                       Em                 G2   G  G4
       Soon you'll hear me knocking at your door.

         G        C                                  F         Em           Dm7 F2/G
Ref.   You just call out my name ... ... and I'll be there.         Yes I will!

             B♭                                    F
Zw.    Now ain't it good to know that you've got a friend
               C                 Cj7
       when people can be so cold.
                F                       B♭7         Am                          D7
       They'll hurt you, yes and desert you and take your soul if you let them,
               Dm7          G
       oh, but don't you let them.

Ref.   You just call out my name ...
```

Am E7
1.When you're down and troub - led and you need
Am E7 Am Dm7
some lov - in' care and no - thing,
G C
no - thing is go - ing right.
Bm7 E7 Bm E7
Close your eyes and think of me and
Am E7 Am Dm7
soon I will be there, to bright - en up e -
Em Gsus2 G Gsus4 G
- ven your dark - est nights. You just call
C F
out my name and you know wher - e - ver I am.
C
I come run - ning to see you a - gain.
Fsus2/G G C CMaj7
Win - ter, spring, sum - mer or fall,

Printed in the EU 2/10 (173137)